INTRODUCTORY GUIDE TO SOLVE MATH PROBLEMS USING TECHNOLOGY

College Algebra

Juan J. Prieto-Valdes

Science & Reading

First Edition / Sep. 2020

Included Materials

1. © Juan J. Prieto-Valdes Pre-Calculus. Library of Congress TXu2014602, US 2016
2. © Juan J. Prieto-Valdes College Algebra. Library of Congress. TXu001880424, US 2013
3. © Juan J. Prieto-Valdes Business Calculus. Library of Congress TXu001954964 US 2014
4. The solutions of the examples using technology were copied directly from the software/engine/app available online. In each case, it is provided the original reference to the webpage/author.

**INTRODUCTORY GUIDE TO SOLVE
MATH PROBLEMS USING TECHNOLOGY**
© Juan J. Prieto Valdes, 2020. All Rights Reserved.
ISBN: 9798689226392

"We need to embrace technology to make learning more engaging. Because when students are engaged and they are interested, that's where learning takes place.

From unknown author

TABLE OF CONTENTS

Introduction:

Learning depends on the interest in gain knowledge that learners have. If you use this guide to formalize a method to copy the answer of mathematical fitness, you will develop a brute skill to complete an assignment. However, using this guide to learn different method of solutions and step-by-step procedures, checking graphical representations and physical meaning of the mathematical exercises will substantially help to develop your mathematical and analytical expertise.

This guide was prepared to give an insight into how to solve math problems using online engines and programs such as Microsoft Mathematics, Wolfram Alpha, Smbolab, etc. As well as different types of apps for intelligent devises, most of them freely available on line.

We will begin with simplest exercises, and gradually will increase the level of difficulty. The following are the most popular technological recourses currently available for learning mathematics on Internet.

WolframAlpha and Algebra and/or Pre-Calculus Course Assistant.

https://products.wolframalpha.com/courseassistants/algebra.html

Using WolframAlpha you can Evaluate any numeric expression or substitute a value for a variable. Simplify fractions, square roots, or any other expression. Solve a simple equation or a system of equations for specific variables. Plot basic, parametric, or polar function(s). Expand any polynomial. Solve equations and simplify expressions. Convert units of length, area, volume, and weight. Factor numeric expressions, polynomials, and symbolic expressions. Divide any two expressions, as well as more advanced operation. We will use Wolfram Alpha online engine and Wolfram Alpha Course Assistant; which can be installed in your phone or any other smart devise.

Microsof Math. Add-in for Word Office.

https://www.microsoft.com/en-us/download/details.aspx?id=17786

Microsoft Mathematics Add-in for Microsoft Word makes it easy to plot graphs in 2D and 3D, solve equations or inequalities, and simplify algebraic expressions in your Word documents and OneNote. Using this add-in you can compute standard mathematical functions, such as roots and logarithms, trigonometric functions, find sums and products of series, matrix and complex numbers operations, solve equations and inequalities, factor polynomials or integers, simplify or expand algebraic expressions, and more advanced operation.

Desmos Graphing Calculator- DG

https://www.desmos.com/

Desmos is an advanced graphing calculator implemented as a web and mobile application. Users can create accounts and save the graphs and plots that they have created. Any algebraic function/expression can be graphically graphed and analyzed.

GeoGebra-GG

https://www.geogebra.org/

GeoGebra is an interactive mathematics software suit for learning science, technology, engineering, and mathematics from primary school up to the university level. Constructions can be made with points, vectors, segments, lines, polygons, conic sections, inequalities, implicit polynomials and functions.

Symbolab-Sy

https://www.symbolab.com/

Symbolab is an answer online engine/service that computes step-by-step solutions to mathematical problems in a range of subjects. Symbolab can interpret a user-entered equation or symbolic problem and find the solution if it exists explaining step by step solution.

Math Solver (Matrix Calculator)-MS

https://www.math10.com/scripts/matrices/determinant-matrix-calculators.html

Math Solver offers solving fraction, metric conversions, power and radical problems. Area and volume of rectangles, circles, triangles, trapezoids, boxes, cylinders, cones, pyramids, spheres. You can simplify and evaluate expressions, and more advanced problems including multiplication, division, and matrix.

.CHAPTER-1. Equations.

1.1. Lines, Slope, and Graphing Linear Functions.

Given two points P_1 and P_2, the slop m of the line passing through these to points can be written as follow:

$$m = \frac{\Delta y}{\Delta x} = \frac{y_2 - y_1}{x_2 - x_1}$$

If considering $P_1(0, b)$ and $P_2(x, y)$, after substituting in previous equation, we get: $m = \frac{y-b}{x-0}$. Solving for y wen get the equation of the line in standard form:

$$y = mx + b$$

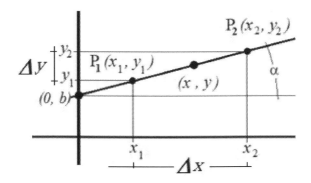

While the equation of the line in general form can be written as follow:

$$ax + by + c = 0$$

Where $m = a/b$

EXAMPLE USING MICROSOFT MATHEMATICS ADD-IN.
GRAPH THE EQUATION $-2x + 4y = 6$ AND FIND THE INTERCEPTS.

Screen shot of Microsoft Mathematics Add-in Tab.

a. Write the equation: Use Insert > Equation and type the equation in Word doc.
b. Open the Mathematics Tab.
c. Highlight the equation you wrote before to graph it.
d. Click on Graph and select Plot in 2D. Check that you are working with REAL numbers
e. When the graph comes up, click INSERT.
f. Calculate the intercepts if needed (manually or use COMPUTE command :

$$At\ x = 0: -2(0) + 4y = 6,\ y = \frac{6}{4}$$

$$At\ y = 0: -2(x) + 4(0) = 6,\ x = -3$$

Check the graph:

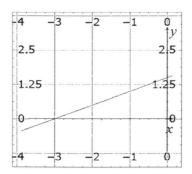

Follow similar procedure to graph any function in 2D. Note that you can vary the settings of your graph: dimension, scale, grid, axis, etc.

EXAMPLE USING WOLFRAM ALPHA ENGINE.
GRAPH THE EQUATION $-2x + 4y = 6$ AND FIND THE INTERCEPTS.

a. Open in your Browser WolframAlpha and type on the search field "Graph and find intercepts: -2x+4y=6".
b. Click Enter.
c. You will get full answer to your question directly (on the next page the screenshot)
d. You can also request "slope", "solve for y", "solve for x", etc.

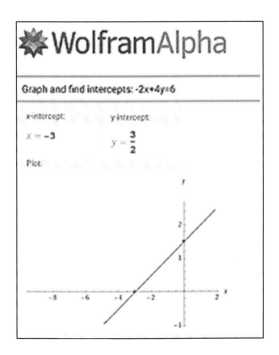

1.2. Solving Linear Equations

A linear equation will have a variable raised to a power of one. A linear equation in one variable can be written in the form $ax + b = 0$ were a and b are real numbers and $a \neq 0$. When the equation has at least one real solution it is called a <u>Conditional Equation</u>. In not conditional, linear equations can be classified depending on the final answer:

<u>**Identity:**</u> An equation is true for all values of x:

$$-4(x + 7) = -4x - 28$$

<u>**Inconsistent Equation:**</u> An equation that is NOT true for any $\mathbb{R}$ number

$$-4(x + 7) = -4x - 21$$

A rational equation involves a variable in the bottom of a fraction. For rational equations you must be sure your answer does not make a denominator go to zero. This is because any number divided by zero is undefined.

$$\frac{11}{x + 3} - 7 = \frac{-3}{x + 3}$$

EXAMPLE USING MICROSOFT MATHEMATICS.
SOLVE THE EQUATION $9x - 20 = 4x + 5$

This is a simple linear equation containing the variable in both sides:

$$9x - 20 = 4x + 5$$

Subtract $4x$ from both sides to get all the variables on one side.

$5x - 20 = 5$, Them, add 20 in both sides, and divide by 5 both sides:

$$5x = 25, \quad \text{simplifying } \frac{5}{5}x = \frac{25}{5}; \text{ so } x = 5$$

Open Mathematics Tab. The equation $9x - 20 = 4x + 5$ on the left represent a line $y_1 = 9x - 20$, and on the right another line, $y_2 = 4x + 5$.

Type both equations, highlight, select graph 2D.

On the right the graph of the lines. They meet (intercept) at $x = 5$, when $y_1 = y_2$, so the solution is $x = 5$.

$$y = 9x - 20$$
$$y = 4x + 5$$

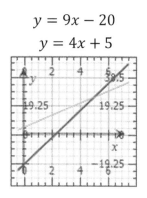

EXAMPLE USING DESMOS GRAPHIC CALCULATOR.

Open Desmos.com. Type both equations in the search field of desmos calculator. Athomaticaly the graph becomes. The interception between these two lines occurs at $x = 5$, confirming that $x = 5$ is the solution.

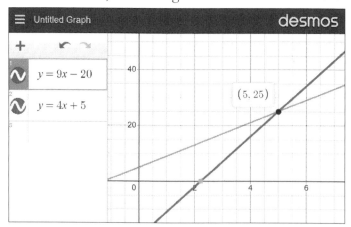

EXAMPLE USING WOLFRAM ALPHA ENGINE.

With wolfram Alpha we can get the graph, the simplification of the original equation and the solution. Type the equation in the search field (only the equation). The engine will answer to all possible questions. On the right you can see resulting WA screen shot of the answer.

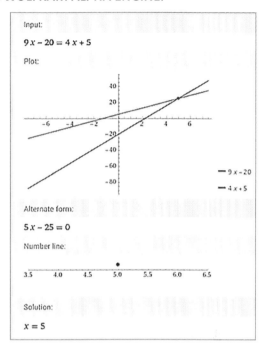

Input:

$9x - 20 = 4x + 5$

Plot:

— $9x - 20$
— $4x + 5$

Alternate form:

$5x - 25 = 0$

Number line:

Solution:

$x = 5$

EXAMPLE USING SYMBOLAB SOLVER.
SOLVE THE EQUATION $2(x - 2) + 11 = x - 4(2x + 5)$.

This is a linear equation which requires distribution. Perform the multiplication and get:

$$2x - 4 + 11 = x - 8x - 20$$

To get all the variables to one side, ad $7x$ to both sides, and them, subtract 7 from both sides to get all the numbers on the right side:

$$9x = -27.$$

Therefore, divide both sides by 9 to get the final answer

$$9/9\, x = (-27)/9 \quad equivalently; \quad x = -3.$$

PROCEDURE:

Open symbolab enging in your browser and type in the search field the equation. Click "**Go**", then "**Show Steps**" command. Symbolab page explain how solve the equation as you can see on the next page (the screen shot):

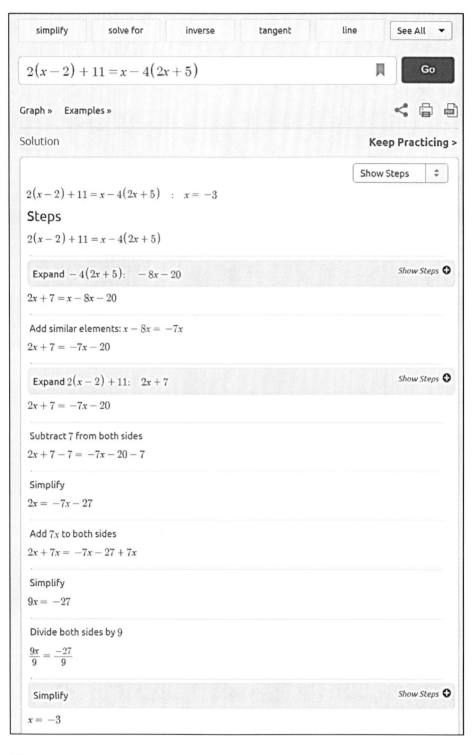

simplify solve for inverse tangent line See All ▼

$$2(x-2)+11 = x - 4(2x+5)$$ 🔖 Go

Graph » Examples »

Solution Keep Practicing >

Show Steps ⬍

$$2(x-2)+11 = x - 4(2x+5) \quad : \quad x = -3$$

Steps

$$2(x-2)+11 = x - 4(2x+5)$$

Expand $-4(2x+5)$: $-8x - 20$ *Show Steps* ➕

$$2x+7 = x - 8x - 20$$

Add similar elements: $x - 8x = -7x$

$$2x+7 = -7x - 20$$

Expand $2(x-2)+11$: $2x+7$ *Show Steps* ➕

$$2x+7 = -7x - 20$$

Subtract 7 from both sides

$$2x+7-7 = -7x - 20 - 7$$

Simplify

$$2x = -7x - 27$$

Add $7x$ to both sides

$$2x+7x = -7x - 27 + 7x$$

Simplify

$$9x = -27$$

Divide both sides by 9

$$\frac{9x}{9} = \frac{-27}{9}$$

Simplify *Show Steps* ➕

$$x = -3$$

1.3. Rational Equations

EXAMPLE USING WOLFRAM ALPHA APP COURSE ASSISTANT.
SOLVE RATIONAL EQUATION
$$\frac{11}{x+3} - 7 = \frac{-3}{x+3}.$$

This is a simple rational equation with the variable on denominator in binomial form. First multiply both sides of the equation by the Lower Common Denominator (LCD).

$$\left(\frac{x+3}{1}\right)\frac{11}{x+3} - \left(\frac{x+3}{1}\right)7 = \left(\frac{x+3}{1}\right)\frac{-3}{x+3}$$

Notice that all the fractions are gone after multiplying, so now solve a resulting simple lineal equation applying previously learned procedures..

$$11 - 7x - 21 = -3$$

$$-7x = 7, \quad dividing\ by\ -7, we\ get:\ x = -1$$

Open the App. Select "**Solve**" and type in the search field the equation. Click GO and you will get the following step by step solution, also you will be able to see graphical solution:

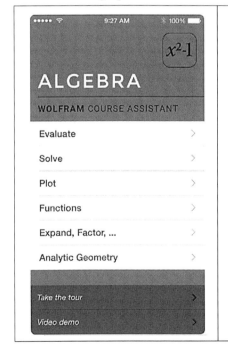

Solve for x:
$$\frac{11}{x+3} - 7 = -\frac{3}{x+3}$$

Multiply both sides by $x + 3$:
$$11 - 7(x+3) = -3$$

Expand out terms of the left hand side:
$$-7x - 10 = -3$$

Add 10 to both sides:
$$-7x = 7$$

Divide both sides by -7:

Answer:
$$x = -1$$

EXAMPLE USING WOLFRAM ALPHA APP COURSE ASSISTANT.

SOLVE RATIONAL EQUATION.

$$\frac{11}{x+6} - \frac{7}{x-2} = \frac{28}{x^2+4x-12}.$$

This is a simple rational equation with the variable on denominator in binomial and factorable trinomial form.

First, we need to find the LCD. If any of the denominators can be factored, we have to do that first. The polynomial can be factored into $(x + 6)(x - 2)$. Now we can see that the LCD is $(x + 6)(x - 2)$.

$$[(x + 6)(x - 2)]\left[\frac{11}{x + 6} - \frac{7}{x - 2} = \frac{28}{(x + 6)(x - 2)}\right]$$

Multiply both sides by the LCD and then reduce each fraction. This will result in a simple linear equation:

$$\frac{11(x - 2)}{1} - \frac{7(x + 6)}{1} = \frac{28}{1}$$

SOLVE THE EQUATION: $11x - 22 - 7x - 42 = 28$, so; $x = 23$

Similar to previous example, get the solution as follow on the right. To simplify (multiplication/division), you have to factor first

$x^2 + 4x - 12 = (x + 6)(x - 2)$

At the end you conclude the operation $x = \frac{92}{4} = 23$, the

Multiply both sides by $x^2 + 4x - 12$:
$11(x - 2) - 7(x + 6) = 28$

Expand out terms of the left hand side:
$4x - 64 = 28$

Add 64 to both sides:
$4x = 92$

solution is $x = 23$.

EXAMPLE USING SYMBOLAB.

SOLVE RATIONAL EQUATION $\dfrac{11}{x+2} - \dfrac{7}{x-2} = \dfrac{-28}{x^2-4}$

This is a rational equation with the variable on denominator (factorable binomial) $x^2 - 4$ can be factored into $(x + 2)(x - 2)$.

The LCD is $(x + 2)(x - 2)$. Multiply both sides by this LCD,

$$[(x + 2)(x - 2)]\left[\frac{11}{x + 2} - \frac{7}{x - 2} = \frac{-28}{(x + 2)(x - 2)}\right]$$

then reduce each fraction by simplifying, this will result in a simple lineal equation.

$$\frac{11(x-2)}{1} - \frac{7(x+2)}{1} = \frac{-28}{1}$$

$$11x - 22 - 7x - 14 = -28$$

Its solution is $= 2$; however this solution have to be rejected because when $x = 2$ the denominator becomes equal to zero, and division by zero is not allowed (undefined).

This example has NO SOLUTION.

Open Symbolab in your browser and type in the search field the equation. Then click Enter. Get general solution as follow, or check for full step-by-step solution:

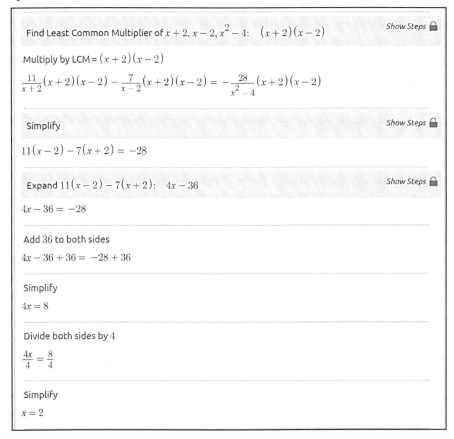

Then, verify the solution.

1.4. Complex Numbers.

COMPLEX NUMBERS ARE COMBINATION OF REAL AND IMAGINARY NUMBER PARTS: $a + bi$, WHERE a AND b ARE REAL NUMBERS.

$$i = \sqrt{-1} \text{ and } i^2 = -1.$$

For any real number $c > 0$; $\sqrt{-c} = i\sqrt{c}$.

Complex numbers can be added, subtracted multiplied and divided. Always we apply algebra rules to perform this operation, we have to combine imaginary part and real part separately; they are two different like terms.

Multiplying (power) i number		
$i^2 = -1$ $i^3 = -i$	$i^4 = 1$ $i^5 = i$	$i^{11} = (i^2)^5 i = -i$ $i^{112} = (i^2)^{56} = 1$

Operations with complex numbers	
Multiplication	**Addition / Subtraction**
Apply algebra considering the number-letter as a variable: $(2 + 2i)(3 - 5i) =$ $= 6 - 10i + 6i - 10i^2$ Because $i^2 = -1$, 10 becomes positive. Then, collect like terms resulting: $16 - 4i$	Apply algebra (distribute if needed), clear parenthesis, and collect like terms $(2 + 2i) + (3 + 5i) = 5 + 7i$ $(5 + 6i) - (3 - 2i) = 2 + 8i$

Division
We have to clear imaginary (complex) numbers from the denominator as we cannot divide by imaginary number. Perform this operation by multiplying both, numerator and denominator by a conjugated expression of the denominator. Then multiply horizontally. Remember that $i^2 = -1$, so you substitute i^2 *by* -1 . $$\frac{(5 + 6i)}{(2 + 3i)} = \frac{(5 + 6i)}{(2 + 3i)} \times \frac{(2 - 3i)}{(2 - 3i)} = \frac{10 - 15i + 12i - 18i^2}{4 - 9i^2}$$ $$= \frac{28 - 3i}{13} = \frac{28}{13} - \frac{3}{13}i$$

Graphic interpretation of the i number:

Find $x - intercepts$ of the graph	Find $x - intercepts$ of the graph
$y = x^2 - 4$	$y = x^2 + 4$
$x - intercepts$ exist when	$x - intercepts$ exist when
$y = 0$, so	$y = 0$, so
$x^2 - 4 = 0$ or $x^2 = 4$	$x^2 + 4 = 0$ or $x^2 = -4$
$\sqrt{x^2} = \pm\sqrt{4}$,	$\sqrt{x^2} = \pm\sqrt{-4}$,
so $x = -2$ or $x = 2$	so $x = -2i$ or $x = 2i$
There are two real value solutions. The graph intercepts the axis x in two places. Graph using MM.	Imaginary solution because there are not real intercepts with axis x. Graph using MM.
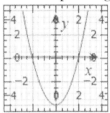	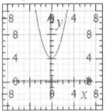

EXAMPLE USING WOLFRAM ALPHA APP COURSE ASSISTANT

DIVIDE (SIMPLIFY) IMAGINARY NUMBERS. $\dfrac{(8-6i)}{(i-4)}$

Use calculation command and type in the search field the equation. Pay attention to the utilization of the conjugate expression (i+4). Observe that the product between complex conjugate numbers produce a real number, allowing to perform the division. Click Done and Compute. Get the following:

Factor 2 out of $8 - 6\,i$ giving $2\,(4 - 3\,i)$:

$$\frac{2\,(-3\,i + 4)}{i - 4}$$

Multiply numerator and denominator of $\dfrac{2\,(-3\,i + 4)}{i - 4}$ by $4 + i$:

$$\frac{2\,(-3\,i + 4)\,(i + 4)}{(i - 4)\,(i + 4)}$$

17

$(-4+i)(4+i) = -4\times4 - 4i + i\times4 + i\times i =$
$-16 - 4i + 4i - 1 = -17:$
$\dfrac{2(-3i+4)(i+4)}{\boxed{-17}}$

$(4-3i)(4+i) = 4\times4 + 4i - 3i\times4 - 3i\times i =$
$16 + 4i - 12i + 3 = 19 - 8i:$
$\dfrac{2\boxed{-8i+19}}{-17}$

Multiply numerator and denominator of $\dfrac{2(-8i+19)}{-17}$ by -1:

Answer:

$$\dfrac{-2(-8i+19)}{17}$$

1.5. Quadratic Equation.

Quadratic equation has the following form $ax^2 + bx + c = 0$:, where a, b, and c are real numbers (coefficients). We solve a quadratic equation using at least 5 different methods.

1.5.1. Factoring and applying ZERO PRODUCT RULE:

When coefficient c = 0 Factor, apply zero product rule to solve	$3x^2 - 4x = 0$ $x(3x - 4) = 0$ $x = 0 \ or \ x = \dfrac{4}{3}$
When a, b, and c coefficients exist Factor, apply zero product rule to solve	$x^2 - 4x - 12 = 0$ $(x - 6)(x + 2) = 0$ $x = -2 \ or \ x = 6$

EXAMPLE USING WOLFRAM ALPHA APP COURSE ASSISTANT.
SOLVE THE EQUATION $x^2 - 4x - 12 = 0$:

Use "Solve" command and type the equation in the search field.

Solve for x: $x^2 - 4x - 12 = 0$

The left hand side factors into a product with two terms: $(x - 6)(x + 2) = 0$

Split into two equations: $x - 6 = 0$ or $x + 2 = 0$

Add 6 to both sides: $x = 6$ or $x + 2 = 0$

Subtract 2 from both sides:

Answer: $x = 6$ or $x = -2$

The App shows the graph. The intercepts $x = 6$ and $x = -2$ are the solutions of the equation. Means, the function is equal to zero:

$$[f(x) = x^2 - 4x - 12 = 0]$$

at x = 6 and x = -2.

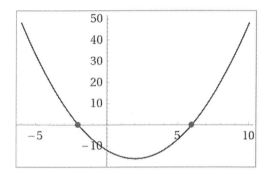

1.5.2. Square Root Property: When $x^2 = $ *numeric value*

$x^2 - 16 = 0 \rightarrow x^2 = 16$ $\sqrt{x^2} = \pm\sqrt{16} \rightarrow x = -4 \text{ or } x = 4$	When coefficient $b = 0$ Apply square root property to solve
$(x - 6)^2 - 25 = 0 \rightarrow (x - 6)^2 = 25$ $\sqrt{(x - 6)^2} = \pm\sqrt{25}$ $x - 6 = \pm 5 \rightarrow x = 6 \pm 5$	Apply square root property to solve and get $x = 1 \text{ or } x = 11$

1.5.3. Completing the Square and using square root property.

In this case we have to construct a Perfect Square Trinomial and make it equal to square of Binomial:

$$ax^2 + bx + c = \left(x + \frac{b}{2}\right)^2. \text{ Where } a = 1.$$

Example 1: $x^2 + 6x - 40 = 0$ $x^2 + 6x + \underline{\ \ } = 40 + \underline{\ \ }$	Note that the coefficient of the term x^2 is equal to one $(a = 1)$. In this case, move 40 to the right, and complete the

19

$x^2 + 6x + 9 = 40 + 9$ $(x + 3)^2 = 49$ $x = -10 \; or \; x = 4$	Left side of the equation by adding required number to create a perfect square trinomial. In this case add $\left(\frac{6}{2}\right)^2 = 9$. Then, transfer the trinomial into a square of binomial and solve applying square root property method.
Example 2: $3x^2 + 15x - 150 = 0$ $\frac{3}{3}x^2 + \frac{15}{3}x - \frac{150}{3} = 0$ $x^2 + \frac{15}{3}x + \frac{25}{4} = \frac{150}{3} + \frac{25}{4}$ $\left(x + \left(\frac{5}{2}\right)\right)^2 = \frac{150(4)}{3(4)} + \frac{25(3)}{4(3)}$ $= \left(\frac{225}{4}\right)$ $\sqrt{\left(x + \left(\frac{5}{2}\right)\right)^2} = \sqrt{\left(\frac{225}{4}\right)}$ $x = -\frac{5}{2} \pm \frac{15}{2}$	If the coefficient in x^2 is different than 1 ($a = 3$), we have to divide the equation by the value of a, to make a new coefficients. The new numbers are $a = 1$, $b = 15/3$ and $c = 150/3$. Then move $\frac{150}{3}$ to the right and add $\frac{25}{4}$ in both parts to complete the square, use the following operation: $\left(\frac{NEW \, b}{2}\right)^2 = \left(\frac{\frac{15}{3}}{2}\right)^2 =$ $\left(\frac{15}{(3)(2)}\right)^2 = \left(\frac{5}{2}\right)^2 = \frac{25}{4}$. By adding $\frac{25}{4}$ to both part of the equation, we create a Perfect Square Polynomial, and we write it in the form of Square of Binomial. Then, solve by applying Square Root Property: $x = -10 \; or \; x = 5$

EXAMPLE USING SYMBOLAB SOLVER
SOLVE BY COMPLETING THE SQUARE $3x^2 + 15x - 150 = 0$

  a.   Open symbolab.com. Use solver.
  b.   Select Solve by completing the square
  c.   Select Show Steps and see the results (displayed on the next page)

The procedure is exactly the same. It is important that you analyze step-by-step if you want to learn mathematics using technology. It is strongly recommended that you open the application in your computer or any other smart devise and repeat the exercise and similar ones.

| Solve by completing the square ⇕ | Show Steps ⇕ |

$3x^2 + 15x - 150 = 0$: $x = 5, x = -10$

Steps

$3x^2 + 15x - 150 = 0$

Add 150 to both sides

$3x^2 + 15x - 150 + 150 = 0 + 150$

Simplify

$3x^2 + 15x = 150$

Divide both sides by 3

$\dfrac{3x^2 + 15x}{3} = \dfrac{150}{3}$

$x^2 + 5x = 50$

Solve by completing the square

Write equation in the form: $x^2 + 2ax + a^2 = (x + a)^2$

Solve for a, $2ax = 5x$: $a = \dfrac{5}{2}$ *Show Steps* ⊕

Add $a^2 = \left(\dfrac{5}{2}\right)^2$ to both sides

$x^2 + 5x + \left(\dfrac{5}{2}\right)^2 = 50 + \left(\dfrac{5}{2}\right)^2$

Simplify $50 + \left(\dfrac{5}{2}\right)^2$: $\dfrac{225}{4}$ *Show Steps* ⊕

$x^2 + 5x + \left(\dfrac{5}{2}\right)^2 = \dfrac{225}{4}$

Complete the square

$\left(x + \dfrac{5}{2}\right)^2 = \dfrac{225}{4}$

For $f^2(x) = a$ the solutions are $f(x) = \sqrt{a},\ -\sqrt{a}$

Solve $x + \dfrac{5}{2} = \sqrt{\dfrac{225}{4}}$: $x = 5$ *Show Steps* ⊕

Solve $x + \dfrac{5}{2} = -\sqrt{\dfrac{225}{4}}$: $x = -10$ *Show Steps* ⊕

The solutions to the quadratic equation are:

$x = 5, x = -10$

1.5.4. By using quadratic formula:

$x_{1,2} = \dfrac{-b \pm \sqrt{b^2 - 4ac}}{2a}$, where a, b, and c are the coefficients (real numbers) in the quadratic equation $ax^2 + bx + c = 0$. The next Table shows the Quadratic Formula demonstration:

We will solve the quadratic equation applying the method described above in point 3 (by completing the square). To facilitate this operation it is convenient to have leading coefficient $= 1$. So, we divide all elements by a, constructing a new equivalent equation	$\dfrac{a}{a}x^2 + \dfrac{b}{a}x + \dfrac{c}{a} = \dfrac{0}{a}$ $x^2 + \dfrac{b}{a}x + \dfrac{c}{a} = 0$
Them, move to the right the constant element; and add in both sides the equivalent value to the square of the half of the new b coefficient, which is: $\left(\dfrac{\frac{b}{a}}{2}\right)^2$; resulting the following equation:	$x^2 + \dfrac{b}{a}x + \quad = -\dfrac{c}{a}$ $x^2 + \dfrac{b}{a}x + \left(\dfrac{b}{2a}\right)^2 =$ $= \left(\dfrac{b}{2a}\right)^2 - \dfrac{c}{a}$
Now, on the left side we have the configuration of a Perfect Square Trinomial which is equal to the square of binomial, while on the right side we multiply and divide the last term by $4a$ to create a common denominator, them perform the addition of the two right elements:	$\left(x + \dfrac{b}{2a}\right)^2 =$ $= \left(\dfrac{b}{2a}\right)^2 - \dfrac{(4a)c}{(4a)a}$ $\left(x + \dfrac{b}{2a}\right)^2 = \dfrac{b^2 - 4ac}{4a^2}$
The new equation can be solved applying the method described above in point 2 (Square Root Property):	$\sqrt{\left(x + \dfrac{b}{2a}\right)^2} = \pm\sqrt{\dfrac{b^2 - 4ac}{4a^2}}$
Solving for x we obtain the quadratic formula:	$x + \dfrac{b}{2a} = \dfrac{\pm\sqrt{b^2 - 4ac}}{2a}$

EXAMPLE USING SYMBOLAB SOLVER.
SOLVE THE EQUATION $3x^2 + 15x - 150 = 0$, USE QUADRATIC FORMULA.

Similar to the previous example (page 20), but now Select the option "Solve with the quadratic formula":

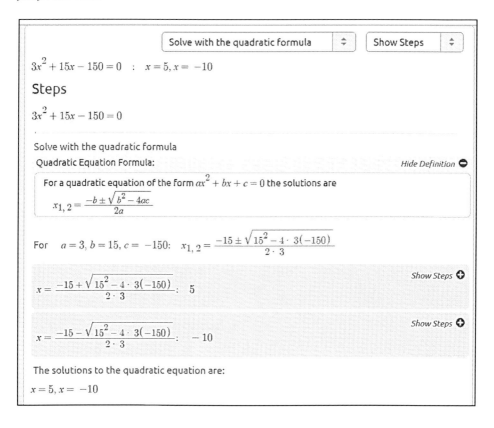

1.6. Radical Equations.

A "radical" equation is an equation in which at least one variable expression is stuck inside a radical, usually a square root. To solve an equation with a radical expression you have to isolate the radical on one side from all other terms and then power (rice to power) both sides of the equation to the level (index) of the radical:

Simple radical value

$\sqrt[3]{x} = 2$ or $x^{1/3} = 2$; Solve by raising both sides to the third power

$\left(\sqrt[3]{x}\right)^3 = 2^3$ because the index of the radical is 3, we power to the third

degree. $\left(x^{1/3}\right)^3 = 2^3$

Resulting: $x = 8$

Radical Equation (generating first degree equation)	Radical Equation (generating 2nd degree equation)
$\sqrt{x+10} + \sqrt{x-6} = 4$ Isolate one of the radicals. $\sqrt{x+10} = 4 - \sqrt{x-6}$ Raise both sides to the second power. $\left(\sqrt{x+10}\right)^2 = \left(4 - \sqrt{x-6}\right)^2$ $x+10 = 16 - 8\sqrt{x-6}$ $+ \left(\sqrt{x-6}\right)^2$ A simple radical equation can be obtained. $x+10 = 16 - 8\sqrt{x-6} + x - 6$ Then, isolate the new radical $\sqrt{x-6}$ and raise it to the second power (to clear the radical). $0 = 8\sqrt{x-6},$ The resulting linear equation has a simple solution $x - 6 = 0,$ so: $x = 6$. It works!	$\sqrt{x+8} - 2 = x$ Isolate the radical $\sqrt{x+8} = x + 2,$ and raise to the second power: $\left(\sqrt{x+8}\right)^2 = (x+2)^2$ $(x+8) = x^2 + 4x + 4,$ collecting like elements: $x^2 + 3x - 4 = 0.$ Factor it and apply zero product rule to solve. $(x+4)(x-1) = 0;$ $x = -4$ or $x = 1$ Finally we have to recheck if the solutions are correct:: for $x = -4$, doesn't work because $\sqrt{-4+8} - 2 \neq -4$ For $x = 1,$ the equation $\sqrt{1+8} - 2 = 1$ is correct. (Reject $x = -4$) $x = 1$ is the only solution

Two-Radical Equation (generating a second degree equation)

$$\sqrt{x-1} - \sqrt{3x+1} = -2;$$

Isolate one of the radicals: $\sqrt{x-1} = \sqrt{3x+1} - 2$

The index is 2. Therefore raise both sides to the second power; resulting a simple radical equation.

$$\left(\sqrt{x-1}\right)^2 = \left(\sqrt{3x+1} - 2\right)^2 \quad \text{and solve the equation:}$$

$$x - 1 = \left(\sqrt{3x+1}\right)^2 - 4\sqrt{3x+1} + 4$$

$x - 1 = 3x + 1 - 4\sqrt{3x + 1} + 4,$ simplifying: $-2x - 6 = -4\sqrt{3x + 1}$

Apply previously described method (raise it one more time to the second power to clear the radical)

$$(x + 3)^2 = \left(2\sqrt{3x + 1}\right)^2; \text{ after expanding will be:}$$

$$x^2 + 6x + 9 = 4(3x + 1)$$

Multiply and collect like elements: $x^2 + 6x + 9 = 12x + 4$.

The resulting quadratic equation can be factored:

$$x^2 - 6x + 5 = (x - 1)(x - 5) = 0;$$

The solutions are: $x = 1 \; or \; x = 5$; Both solutions work

---

Two-Radical Equation (generating a second degree equation)

First raise to the second power both sides of the equation:	$1 + \sqrt{x + 4} = \sqrt{3x + 1}$
Then, expand and simplify:	$\left(1 + \sqrt{x + 4}\right)^2 =$
to get a new radical equation:	$\left(\sqrt{3x + 1}\right)^2$
Divide by 2 and power one more time to the second degree:	$1 + 2\sqrt{x + 4} + \left(\sqrt{x + 4}\right)^2 = 3x + 1$
Multiply, collect like terms and get new equation:	$2\sqrt{x + 4} = 2x - 4$
Solved by factoring.	$\left(\sqrt{x + 4}\right)^2 = (x - 2)^2$
so $x = 0 \; or \; 5$	$x + 4 = x^2 - 4x + 4,$
After checking, $x = 5$ and $x = 0$ both work	$x^2 - 5x = 0, \quad x^2 - 5x = x(x - 5) = 0$

EXAMPLE USING WOLFRAM ALPHA APP COURSE ASSISTANT
SOLVE RATIONAL EQUATION
$$1 + \sqrt{x + 4} = \sqrt{3x + 1}$$

Open your Algebra Course Assistant, or Pre-Calculus Course Assistant. Select Solve and type the equation in the search field. After typing select Done and Compute. Look to the result:

Solve for x:

$$\sqrt{x+4} + 1 = \sqrt{3x+1}$$

Raise both sides to the power of 2:

$$\left(\sqrt{x+4} + 1\right)^2 = 3x+1$$

Subtract $3x+1$ from both sides:

$$-1 - 3x + \left(\sqrt{x+4} + 1\right)^2 = 0$$

$$-1 - 3x + \left(\sqrt{x+4} + 1\right)^2 = 4 - 2x + 2\sqrt{x+4}:$$

$$4 - 2x + 2\sqrt{x+4} = 0$$

Simplify and substitute $y = \sqrt{x+4}$.

$$4 - 2x + 2\sqrt{x+4} = 12 + 2\sqrt{x+4} - 2\left(\sqrt{x+4}\right)^2$$

$$= -2y^2 + 2y + 12:$$

$$-2y^2 + 2y + 12 = 0$$

The left hand side factors into a product with three terms:

$$-2(y-3)(y+2) = 0$$

Divide both sides by -2:

$$(y-3)(y+2) = 0$$

Divide both sides by -2:

$$(y-3)(y+2) = 0$$

Split into two equations:

$$y - 3 = 0 \quad \text{or} \quad y + 2 = 0$$

Add 3 to both sides:

$$\boxed{y = 3} \quad \text{or} \quad y + 2 = 0$$

Substitute back for $y = \sqrt{x+4}$:

$\sqrt{x+4} = 3$ or $y + 2 = 0$

Raise both sides to the power of two:

$x + 4 = 9$ or $y + 2 = 0$

Subtract 4 from both sides:

$x = 5$ or $y + 2 = 0$

Subtract 2 from both sides:

$x = 5$ or $y = -2$

Substitute back for $y = \sqrt{x+4}$:

$x = 5$ or $\sqrt{x+4} = -2$

Raise both sides to the power of two:

$x = 5$ or $x + 4 = 4$

Subtract 4 from both sides:

$x = 5$ or $x = 0$

$\sqrt{x+4} + 1 \Rightarrow \sqrt{4+0} + 1 = 3$
$\sqrt{3x+1} \Rightarrow \sqrt{1+3 \times 0} = 1$:
So this solution is incorrect

$\sqrt{x+4} + 1 \Rightarrow \sqrt{4+5} + 1 = 4$
$\sqrt{3x+1} \Rightarrow \sqrt{1+3 \times 5} = 4$:
So this solution is correct

The solution is:

Answer:

$x = 5$

The Application also provides the graph by considering two radical functions. Their intercepts will be the solution:

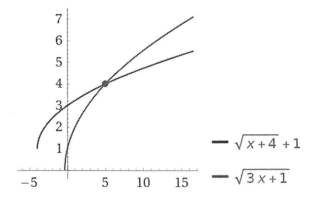

1.7. Other Types of Equations

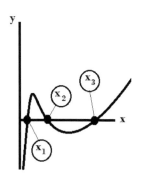

Solving an algebra equation sometimes means to find the interceptions of the graph with the axis x. To solve an equation, we can create a fictitious function and analyze its graph, or we make it equal to zero ($y = 0$) to later apply zero-product rule. The function interpretation is useful to understand the problem. Let's consider that our function is equal to zero:

$$y = Algebra\ expression = 0.$$

If the equation is 3rd degree, for example
$$(y = a_3x^3 + a_2x^2 + a_1x + a_0 = 0)$$

Where a_1, a_2 , etc… are real coefficients. This equation could have 3, 2, or 1 real solution, (how many times it cuts the axis x). On the graphs are displayed $x_1,$ $x_2,$ and x_3 interceptions. Equations can be of any degree; however, in this topic, to facilitate the solution process, we will use a second degree interpretation, factorable by substituting the variable or by creating a common term (factor that could be considered of a second or first degree). The following are some descriptive examples:

28

Third degree equation, factorable by grouping

$$4x^3 + 16x^2 = 16x + 64$$

Create the function and make it equal to zero, then, factor by grouping.

$$4x^3 + 16x^2 - 16x - 64 = 0$$

To factor, regroup in two and two terms, then factor using a convenient Common Factor to produce the same binomial combination.

$4x^2(x + 4) - 16(x + 4) = 0$ equivalently to: $(x + 4)(4x^2 - 16) = 0$. Then factor:

$$(x + 4)(2x + 4)(2x - 4) = 0$$

Finally, Apply zero-product rule to solve the equation.

$$x = -4 \text{ or } x = -2 \text{ or } x = 2$$

EXAMPLE USING WOLFRAM ALPHA ENGINE
SOLVE THE EQUATION $4x^3 + 16x^2 = 16x + 64$

For graphic solution the engine consider two functions: from the right third degree equation and from the right linear equation:

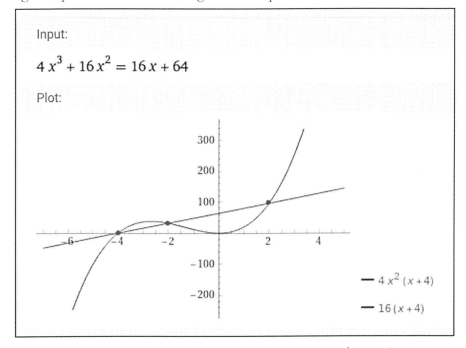

The interceptions/solutions are $x = -4$, $x = -2$, and $x = 2$.

Using the option step by step solution we get:

STEP 1

Solve for x over the real numbers:

$4x^3 + 16x^2 = 16x + 64$

STEP 2

> Hint: Move everything to the left hand side.

Subtract $16x + 64$ from both sides:

$4x^3 + 16x^2 - 16x - 64 = 0$

We can also check step-by-step factorization process. It is recommended that student open the application/software and recheck what is described in this guide for working with technology.

STEP 3

> Hint: Factor the left hand side.

The left hand side factors into a product with four terms:

$4(x - 2)(x + 2)(x + 4) = 0$

STEP 4

> Hint: Divide both sides by a constant to simplify the equation.

Divide both sides by 4:

$(x - 2)(x + 2)(x + 4) = 0$

STEP 5

> **Hint:** Find the roots of each term in the product separately.

Split into three equations:

$x - 2 = 0$ or $x + 2 = 0$ or $x + 4 = 0$

STEP 6

> **Hint:** Look at the first equation: Solve for x.

Add 2 to both sides:

$\boxed{x = 2}$ or $x + 2 = 0$ or $x + 4 = 0$

STEP 7

> **Hint:** Look at the second equation: Solve for x.

Subtract 2 from both sides:

$x = 2$ or $\boxed{x = -2}$ or $x + 4 = 0$

STEP 8

> **Hint:** Look at the third equation: Solve for x.

Subtract 4 from both sides:

Answer:

$x = 2$ or $x = -2$ or $\boxed{x = -4}$

Four degree equation, factorable using variable replacement

$$x^4 - 29x^2 + 100 = 0$$

Replace the variable to convert 4th degree equation in quadratic form. $u =$
$$x^2 \ or \ u^2 = x^4 \ )$$

$u^2 - 29u + 100 = 0$, which can ben factored as the product of two binomials: $(u - 25)(u - 4) = 0$

Apply zero product rule and solve: $u = 25 \ or \ u = 4$

After having resulted u. Substitute these values into variable replacement equation $(u = x^2)$

and get final solution using square root property

$$25 = x^2 \ and \ 4 = x^2$$

$$x = -5 \ or \ x = 5 \ or \ x = -2 \ or \ x = 2$$

The equation also can be solved using direct factorization
(no variable replacement):

$$x^4 - 29x^2 + 100 = (x - 5)(x + 5)(x - 2)(x + 2) = 0$$

Where: $x = -2 \ or \ x = 2 \ or \ x = -5 \ or \ x = 5$

Binomial second degree equation, factorable using variable replacement

$$(3x + 3)^2 - 4(3x + 3) - 12 = 0$$

Replace the variable to convert 4th degree equation in quadratic form:
$$(u = 3x + 3).$$

$$(u)^2 - 4(u) - 12 = 0$$

Factor the new equation and solve for u

$$(u + 2)(u - 6) = 0 \quad \text{so} \quad u = -2 \ or \ u = 6$$

From replacement equation we get two simple lineal equations::

$$-2 = 3x + 3 \quad \text{and} \ 6 = 3x + 3 \text{So:} \quad x = -\frac{5}{3} \ or \ x = 1$$

$$\text{So:} \quad x = -\frac{5}{3} \ or \ x = 1$$

Binomial Four degree equation, factorable using variable replacement

$$(x^2 - 9)^2 - 8(x^2 - 9) + 12 = 0$$

Convert 4th degree equation in quadratic form replacing $u = x^2 - 9$.

$$u^2 - 8u + 12 = 0$$

Factor new equation and solve applying zero product rule

$$u = 2 \ or \ u = 6$$

After having resulted u; substitute these values into variable replacement equation $(u = x^2 - 9)$ and get final solution using square root property.

$$2 = x^2 - 9 \quad and \quad 6 = x^2 - 9$$

So, The solutions will be:

$$x = \sqrt{11} \ or \ x = -\sqrt{11} \quad or \quad x = \sqrt{15} \ or \ x = -\sqrt{15}$$

Rational equation factorable as quadratic in form

$$x^{\frac{2}{3}} + 5x^{\frac{1}{3}} - 6 = 0$$

Convert radical equation in quadratic form: $\left(x^{\frac{1}{3}}\right)^2 + 5\left(x^{\frac{1}{3}}\right) - 6 = 0$

Replace $u = x^{\frac{1}{3}}$ and get $u^2 + 5u - 6 = 0,$

solve by factoring $(u + 6)(u - 1) = 0$

$$u = -6 \ or \ u = 1$$

After having resulted u ; substitute these values into variable replacement equation

$\left(u = \left(x^{\frac{1}{3}}\right)\right)$ and get final solution using the root property.

$$-6 = x^{\frac{1}{3}} \ and \ 1 = x^{\frac{1}{3}} \ , \ -6 = \sqrt[3]{x} \ and \ 1 = \sqrt[3]{x}$$

$$or \ x = -216 \quad and \quad x = 1$$

EXAMPLE USING WOLFRAM ALPHA ENGINE.
SOLVE THE EQUATION. $x^{-2} + 10x^{-1} + 21 = 0$

The engine graphically solves the function as illustrated in the next page.

The graph shows the solutions. However, using the option step-by-step solution you can see analytic solution as follow:

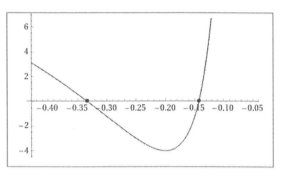

Solutions:

STEP 1

Solve for x over the real numbers:

$$21 + \frac{10}{x} + \frac{1}{x^2} = 0$$

STEP 2

Hint: Write the left hand side as a single fraction.

Bring $21 + \frac{10}{x} + \frac{1}{x^2}$ together using the common denominator x^2:

$$\frac{21x^2 + 10x + 1}{x^2} = 0$$

STEP 3

Hint: Multiply both sides by a polynomial to clear fractions.

Multiply both sides by x^2:

$$21x^2 + 10x + 1 = 0$$

STEP 4

Hint: Factor the left hand side.

The left hand side factors into a product with two terms:

$$(3x + 1)(7x + 1) = 0$$

STEP 5

> **Hint:** Find the roots of each term in the product separately.

Split into two equations:

$3x + 1 = 0$ or $7x + 1 = 0$

STEP 6

> **Hint:** Look at the first equation: Isolate terms with x to the left hand side.

Subtract 1 from both sides:

$\boxed{3x = -1}$ or $7x + 1 = 0$

STEP 7

> **Hint:** Solve for x.

Divide both sides by 3:

$\boxed{x = -\dfrac{1}{3}}$ or $7x + 1 = 0$

STEP 8

> **Hint:** Look at the second equation: Isolate terms with x to the left hand side.

Subtract 1 from both sides:

$x = -\dfrac{1}{3}$ or $\boxed{7x = -1}$

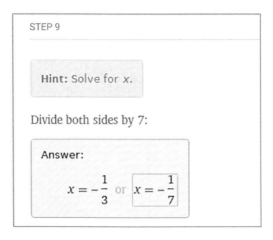

STEP 9

Hint: Solve for x.

Divide both sides by 7:

Answer:

$$x = -\frac{1}{3} \quad \text{or} \quad x = -\frac{1}{7}$$

1.8. Absolute Value Equations & Inequalities.

Absolute value equations. To solve an absolute value equation, isolate the absolute value on one side of the equal sign, and establish (create) two cases as follow: for $|f(x)| = a$, create:

$$\text{Case 1:} \quad f(x) = a \qquad \text{Case 2:} \quad f(x) = -a$$

CHECK your answers for the two "derived" equations. Also try to use graphic interpretation by plotting: $y_1 = f(x)$, $y_2 = -f(x)$, and $y_3 = a$ in the x, y coordinate system. In the second example below this method id applied..

Inequalities. To solve an inequality we can use numeric and/or graphic interpretations:

Numeric solution of an inequality is a number (or group of numbers) which when substituted for the variable makes the inequality a true statement.

Graphically: $g(x) > f(x)$, means, when $g(x)$ is/goes over $f(x)$; check the graph and note that the set of numbers

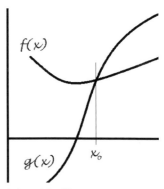

(x_0, ∞) satisfy the inequality. The figure on the right side illustrates general case, however, in this topic we will work only with linear equations. The following examples illustrate the solution procedures of Absolute value equations, and inequalities:

Simple absolute value equations-and graphic interpretation

$9\lvert x - 3\rvert = 36 \rightarrow \lvert x - 3\rvert = 4$ $+(x - 3) = 4$ and $-(x - 3) = 4$ $x - 3 = 4$ and $-x + 3 = 4$ $x = 7$ and $x = -1$ **In one line case solution:** $-4 = x - 3 = 4$ $+3 \dots \quad + 3 \dots \quad + 3$ ——————————— $-1 = x = 7$	Isolate the absolute value part of the equation; in this case $\lvert x - 3\rvert$. Consider that it content can be positive as well as negative by creating two new linear equations. Solve them isolating the variable. Note that the absolute value equation can be solve in one line creating a compound equation, later by adding +3 in all sides +3 for this specific case).
$\lvert 2(x + 1) + 8\rvert = 16$ $-[2(x + 1) + 8] = 16$ and $[2(x + 1) + 8] = 16$ $-2x - 10 = 16$ and $2x + 10 = 16$ $x = -13$ and $x = 3$ 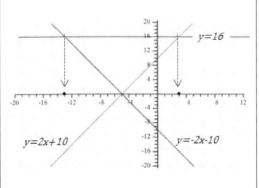	Isolate the absolute value part of the equation; in this case $\lvert 2x + 10\rvert$. Consider that it content can be negative (on the left) as well as positive (right) by creating two new linear equations. Solve each isolating the variable. Graphically we can consider three equations: $y_1 = -2x - 10$ $y_2 = 2x + 10$ $y_3 = 16$ This example can be considered as a system of three linear equations. Graphing them, we can see the solution at the interceptions between y_1 and y_3 AND y_2 and Y_3.

Solving the inequality and graphing the result to show the solution set
In number line, in inequality and/or set representation.

Simple monomial/number	
$$\|x\| < 2$$ x can be positive and negative: $x < 2$ AND $-x < 2$ Note that $-x < 2$ is equivalent to $x > -2$ 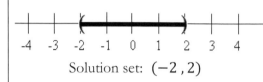 Solution set: $(-2, 2)$	multiplying by -1 both sides of the second inequality we get $$-(1)(-x) < -(1)(2)$$ and swish the inequality symbol $$x > -2$$
$$\|x\| > 2$$ x can be positive and negative; in both cases greater than 2. $x > 2$ OR $-x > 2$ (equivalent to $x < -2$) 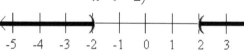	We have to remember the multiplication/division property of inequalities: When **multiplying or dividing** by a negative number, we have to change the direction of the inequality. In this case the answer (solution set) will be: $$(-\infty, -2) \; or \; (2, \infty)$$

Simple Binomial

$$\|x - 6\| > 2$$ $x - 6 > 2$ AND $-x + 6 > 2$ $x > 8$ or $-x > -4$ (equivalent to $x < 4$) are solutions 	**N**ote when we use AND and OR, depending of the type of solution: this is a resulting interception set (in this case the solutions are in both sets) or two independent set are solutions (in this case the solution can be ascribed to one OR another set).

Previous example can be solved in one line	
$$-2 > x - 6 > 2$$ $$\underline{+6 \qquad +6 \qquad +6}$$ $$4 > x > 8$$ Add 6 in each section and we get the result automatically. On the infinity side use parenthesis because we never touch the infinite. Always use parenthesis to represent **greater than** or **less than**. Solution in set notation can be written as: $(-\infty, 4)\ or\ (8, \infty)$.	When using **greater than or equal** the corresponding symbol will be bracket as displayed in a following supplementary example/solution: $4 \geq x \geq 8$ can be represented using set notation as $(-\infty,\ 4]\ or\ [8,\ \infty)$.

. **EXAMPLE USING SYMBOLAB SOLVER.**
SOLVE ABSOLUTE VALUE EQUATION $|3X-8|+12 \leq 19$

Open Synbolab.com. Write in the search field the inequality. Get the solution.

You also can solve graphically considering three equations, similar to example in page 39.

$$y = 3x - 4$$
$$y = -3x + 20$$
$$y = 19$$

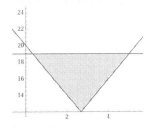

Subtract 12 from both sides $$|3x - 8| + 12 - 12 \leq 19 - 12$$
Simplify $$|3x - 8| \leq 7$$
Apply absolute rule: If $|u| \leq a, a > 0$ then $-a \leq u \leq a$ $$-7 \leq 3x - 8 \leq 7$$ $$3x - 8 \geq -7 \quad \text{and} \quad 3x - 8 \leq 7$$
$$3x - 8 \geq -7 \ : \ x \geq \tfrac{1}{3}$$
$$3x - 8 \leq 7 \ : \ x \leq 5$$
Combine the intervals $$x \geq \tfrac{1}{3} \quad \text{and} \quad x \leq 5$$
Merge Overlapping Intervals $$\tfrac{1}{3} \leq x \leq 5$$

CHAPTER-2.

Functions and Graphing Techniques.

2.1. The Distance, Midpoint, and Circles.

The Distance Formula is a variant of the Pythagorean Theorem $(c^2 = a^2 + b^2)$ that you used before in geometry to find the length of the hypotenuse of a right triangle. Given the two points $P_1(x_1, y_1)$ and $P_2(x_2, y_2)$, the distance between these points is given by the formula:

$$d^2_{P_1-P_2} = (x_2 - x_1)^2 + (y_2 - y_1)^2$$

$$d_{P_1-P_2} = \sqrt{(x_2 - x_1)^2 + (y_2 - y_1)^2}$$

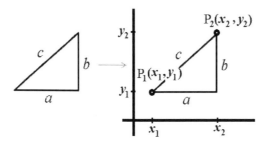

Where $a = (x_2 - x_1)$ and $b = (y_2 - y_1)$. Whichever one you call "first" or "second" point, is up to you; the distance will be the same because the distance is an absolute (scalar) value, not depending of direction.

Example 1: given two points located at (-2,1) and (3,6) find the distance between them.

Applying the distance formula we get:

$$d = \sqrt{(3 + 2)^2 + (6 - 1)^2} = 5\sqrt{2}$$

Middle Point: Middle Point of the segment line is located at:

$$x_M = \frac{(x_2 + x_1)}{2} \quad and \quad y_M = \frac{(y_2 + y_1)}{2}.$$

In example-1, the middle point is located at:

$$x_M = \frac{(3-2)}{2} = 0.5 \quad and \quad y_M = \frac{(6+1)}{2} = 3.5 \text{ ;so } (x_M, y_M) \equiv (0.5, 3.5)$$

Circles: To write the equation of circle first we need to know-- "what is a circle?"

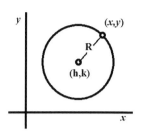

If you cannot answer to this question, you never will be able to write the equation of the circle. *Circle is a line, equidistant to one fixed point called center. The fixed distance between any $(x.y)$ point of the line and the center (h, k) is called the radius. We can rewrite the equation of the circle using the distance between two points:*

$$R = \sqrt{(x - h)^2 + (y - k)^2} \quad \text{or} \quad (x - h)^2 + (y - k)^2 = R^2,$$

which is the equation of the circle in standard form.

Example 1: Write the equation of the circle with center at $(2, 4)$ and radios equal to 4.

By substituting in a previously developed formula we get:

$$(x - 2)^2 + (y - 4)^2 = 16.$$

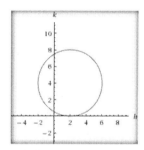

Example 2: Graph the circle given its equation in general form:

$$x^2 + y^2 + 6x + 10y - 15 = 0$$

We can provide x values and calculate y, but the work will be tedious and very consuming time. Notable easier will be by completing the square to create a two binomial expression, with another words, re-write the equation in a standard form by completing the square. To complete the square we can use :

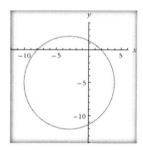

$$\left(\frac{6}{2}\right)^2 = 9 \ and \ \left(\frac{10}{2}\right)^2 = 25$$

Resulting: $x^2 + 6x + 9 + y^2 + 10y + 25 = 15 + 9 + 25$

or in binomial form:

$$(x + 3)^2 + (y + 5)^2 = 49.$$

As we can see, the center is located at $(h, k) = (-3, -5)$,

and the radius $R = 7$ units.

EXAMPLE USING WOLFRAM ALPHA ENGINE.
WRITE THE CHARACTERISTICS OF THE GIVEN EQUATION/CIRCLE
$$x^2 + y^2 - x - 4y = 20$$

Open Wolfram Alpha in your browser and type the equation in the search field. The step by step solution can be requested by completing the square or by solving the equation.

characteristics of the circle: x^2+y^2-x-4 y=20

∫π̃ Extended Keyboard   ⬆ Upload

Assuming "circle" is a geometric object | Use as a unit instead

Input interpretation:

| circle | Cartesian equation $x^2 + y^2 - x - 4y = 20$ |

Visual representation:

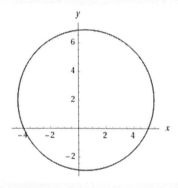

Properties:

center	$\left(\frac{1}{2}, 2\right) = (0.5, 2)$
radius	$\dfrac{\sqrt{97}}{2} \approx 4.92443$
diameter	$\sqrt{97} \approx 9.84886$
area enclosed	$\dfrac{97\pi}{4} \approx 76.1836$
circumference	$\sqrt{97}\,\pi \approx 30.9411$

2.2. Functions and Their Graph.

Quick description of the concept:

A function from X into Y is a relation that associates with each element of X exactly one element of Y. The idea of a function machine is often helpful for conveying the notion of a function. The machine applies the rule that assigns to each member of a set called the **domain** (x) exactly one member of a set called the **range** (y).

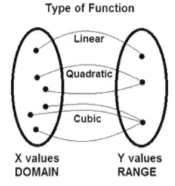

Type of Function

You can produce ONE juice from different fruits (one, two, or more flavors), but you cannot produce different types of juices (one, two, or more different juices) from the same (one) fruit. The first case is an example of a function (**only one y**). An

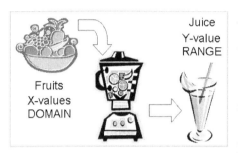

equation can serve as a function if it assigns each x value (one or more) exactly only one y value.

Examples of lineal, quadratic and rational functions:

LINEAR Functions (1st degree) one x value for each y value	QUADRATIC Functions (2nd degree function) two x values for each y value	RATIONAL Functions
$y = \frac{2}{3}x + 3$ => $f(x) = \frac{2}{3}x + 3$ $f(x) = \frac{2}{3}x + 3$ $f(3) = \frac{2}{3}(3) + 3 = 5$ Domain: $\{x \mid x \in \text{any reals}\}$	$f(x) = -20x^2 + 80x$ $f(1) = -20(1)^2 + 80(1) = 60$ $f(3) = -20(3)^2 + 80(3) = 60$ The Domain and Range will be: $\{0 \le x \le 4\}$ and $\{0 \le y \le 80\}$	$f(x) = \frac{2x - 1}{x + 2}$ At $x = 2$, $f(x) = \text{und}$ The Domain: $\{x \mid x \in reals, x \ne -2\}$

Previous three functions can be graphed as follow:

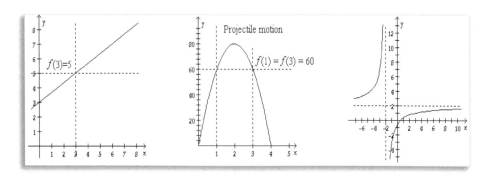

2.3. Graphing Technics and Transformation of Functions.

The following examples are the simplest case of transformation.

Translating a graph vertically (up / down)

Given Original Simple Function: $y = x^2$.

When $y = 0$, we get: $x = 0$.

One solution, one interception with axis x at $(0,0)$

Same function adding two units: $y = x^2 + 2$. In this case, you have to move the graph two units up, as we are subtracting two units to the y value $(y - 2 = x^2)$.

When $y = 0$ we get complex solutions. no real solution, means no interception with axis x). At $x^2 + 2 = 0$, we get $(x^2 = -2)$ two solutions: $x = \pm\sqrt{2}\, i$. **Same function** subtracting two units: $y = x^2 - 2$. Move two unit down as we are adding two units to the y ($y + 2 = x^2$). When $y = 0$ $(x^2 - 2 = 0)$, we get two real solutions, means two interceptions with axis x at: $x = \sqrt{2}$ or $x = -\sqrt{2}$	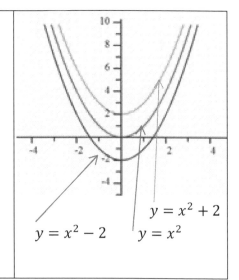 $y = x^2 + 2$ $y = x^2 - 2$ $y = x^2$

Translating a graph horizontally (to the right or to the left)

$y = x^2$, adding/subtracting two (2) units to the x:

When subtracting: $y = (x - 2)^2$, you have to move the graph two units to the right.

If adding, $y = (x + 2)^2$, you have to move the graph two units to the left.

$$y = (x + 2)^2 \qquad y = x^2$$
$$y = (x - 2)^2$$

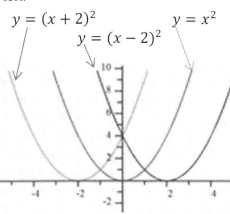

Stretch or Compress

In $y = ax^2$, if a>1, stretch. If a<1 shrink (compress). If $y = 2x^2$, we have to multiply the ordinate y by 2,

$$y = 2x^2$$

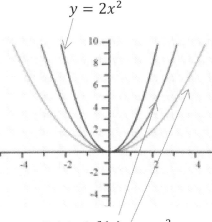

Original $f(x)$ $y = x^2$

or divide the ordinate y by 2 when $y = \frac{1}{2}x^2$

Reflecting a graph horizontally

Towards axis y when replacing x with $-x$

$$y = \sqrt{-x} \qquad y = \sqrt{x}$$

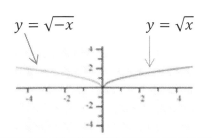

Reflecting a graph vertically

When replacing y with $-y$.

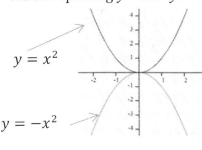

$$y = x^2$$

$$y = -x^2$$

EXAMPLE USING WOLFRAM ALPHA ENGINE.
ANALYZE TRANSFORMATION OF FUNCTIONS

You can transform any function using Function Transformation Project:

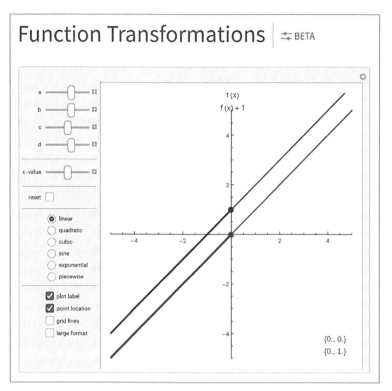

https://demonstrations.wolfram.com/FunctionTransformations/

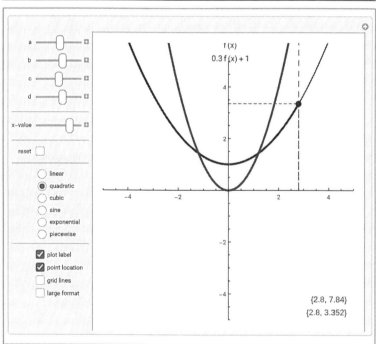

2.4. General Characteristics of Functions

Even symmetry	Odd symmetry
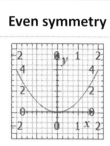	
The graph of the equation $y = x^2$ is symmetric with respect to the $y - axis$ if substituting x for $-x$ in the equation results in an equivalent equation (same y):	The graph of the equation $y = x^3$ is symmetric with respect to the origin if substituting x for $-x$ and y for $-y$ in the equation, the new one results in an equivalent equation (same y)
$$f(x)=f(-x)$$	$$f(x)=-f(-x)$$

Increasing	Decreasing	Constant	Max. & Min.
From $x = 7$ to $x = 10$ the function is increasing	From $x = 1$ to $x = 7$ the function is decreasing	From $-\infty$ to $+\infty$ the function is constant	Maximum at $x = 1$, and Minimum at $x = 7$

2.5. Combination and Composition of Functions.

The sum, difference, product, or quotient of functions are arithmetic operations with functions:

1. **Sum:** $(f + g)(x) = f(x) + g(x)$
2. **Difference:** $(f - g)(x) = f(x) - g(x)$
3. **Product:** $(f \cdot g)(x) = f(x) \cdot g(x)$
4. **Quotient:** $(f / g)(x) = f(x) / g(x)$, as long as $g(x)$ isn't zero.

Example: Let f be the function $f(x) = x^2 + 1$ and g be the function $g(x) = x + 3$, then

$$(f + g)(x) = x^2 + x + 4,$$
$$(f - g)(x) = x^2 - x - 2,$$
$$(f \cdot g)(x) = x^3 + 3x^2 + x + 3,$$
$$(f / g)(x) = \frac{x^2 + 1}{x + 3}$$

5. **Composition:** $(f \circ g)(x) = f\big(g(x)\big)$

The composition of two functions f and g is the new function we get by performing f first, and then performing g.

Example: Let $f(x) = x^2 + 1$ and $g(x) = x + 3$, then the composition of g with f will be:

$$f\big(g(x)\big) = f(x + 3) = (x + 3)^2 + 1 = x^2 + 6x + 10.$$
$$g\big(f(x)\big) = g(x^2 + 1) = x^2 + 1 + 3 = x^2 + 4$$

The domain of each of these combinations/composition is the intersection of the domain of $f(x)$ and the domain of $g(x)$. In other words, both functions must be defined at a point for the combination to be defined.

TECHNOLOGY: STUDY THE CHARACTERISTICS OF FUNCTIONS USING WOLFRAM ALPHA ONLINE ENGINE.

https://www.wolframalpha.com/examples/mathematics/mathematical-functions/

CHAPTER 3.

Polynomial Functions. Properties.

3.1. Quadratic Functions.

In Topic 1.5-3 we demonstrated the Quadratic Formula

$$x_{1,2} = \frac{-b \pm \sqrt{b^2 - 4ac}}{2a}$$

by solving the quadratic function

$$f(x) = ax^2 + bx + c \text{ at } f(x) = 0 .$$

We used the method of completing the square.

Similar to that case for any $f(x)$ different than zero, we can write:

$$f(x) = ax^2 + bx + c = a\left(x^2 + \frac{b}{a}x + \frac{c}{a}\right)$$

$$= a\left(x^2 + \frac{b}{a}x + \left(\frac{b}{2a}\right)^2 - \left(\frac{b}{2a}\right)^2 + \frac{c}{a}\right)$$

$$= a\left(x + \frac{b}{2a}\right)^2 + \left(\frac{-b^2 + 4ac}{4a}\right)$$

Analogous to the standard form equation of the circle, previous equation can be written as:

$$f(x) = a(x - h)^2 + k ;$$

This is the standard form of the equation of the parabola, which vertex is located at $(h, k) = \left(-\frac{b}{2a}, \frac{-b^2+4ac}{4a}\right)$. It is easier to evaluate the coordinate x of the vertex from $h = x_v = -\frac{b}{2a}$, and them evaluate y coordinate:

$$k = y_v = f(x_v).$$

The relation $x_v = -\frac{b}{2a}$ also can be obtained using the middle point between zero solutions $x_{1,2}$:

$$x_v = \frac{x_1 + x_2}{2} = \frac{\frac{-b - \sqrt{b^2 - 4ac}}{2a} + \frac{-b + \sqrt{b^2 - 4ac}}{2a}}{2}$$

$$= \frac{-b - \sqrt{b^2 - 4ac} - b + \sqrt{b^2 - 4ac}}{4a} = \frac{-b}{2a}$$

Example: Graph: $y = 3x^2 + 6x + 12$

First find the vertex position: $x_v = -\frac{b}{2a} = -\frac{6}{2(3)} = -1$

Secondly; find the intercepts: Y (making $x = 0$) and (X making $y = 0$), for X you have to solve the equation. Use quadratic formula. Both answers are complex (imaginary component) because no interception with axis x.

$$y_v = f(-1) = 3(-1)^2 + 6(1-) + 12 = 9$$
$$\text{So: } (x_v, y_v) = (-1, 9)$$

$Y_{int.(exist\ at\ x=0)} = 12$ and $X_{int.(exist\ at\ y=0)};\ 3x^2 + 6x + 12 = 0$

Solve using quadratic equation:

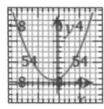

$$x_{1,2} = \frac{-b \pm \sqrt{b^2 - 4ac}}{2a} = \frac{-6 \pm \sqrt{6^2 - 4(3)(12)}}{2(3)} =$$
$$= \frac{-6 \pm \sqrt{-108}}{6} = \frac{-6 \pm \sqrt{-(36)(3)}}{6} = \frac{-6 \pm 6\sqrt{-3}}{6}$$
$$x_1 = -\sqrt{3}\,i - 1 \text{ or } x_2 = -1 + \sqrt{3}\,i$$

Example: Graph: $y = 3x^2 + 6x - 12$

First find the vertex position. Secondly; find the intercepts: Y (making $x = 0$) and (X making $y = 0$), for X you have to solve the equation. Use quadratic formula. Both answers are real numbers

$$x_v = -\frac{b}{2a} = -\frac{6}{2(3)} = -1$$
$$y_v = f(-1) = 3(-1)^2 + 6(1-) - 12 = -15$$
$$\text{So: } (x_v, y_v) = (-1, -15)$$
$$Y_{intercept\,(exist\ at\ x=0)} = -12$$
$$X_{intercept\,(exist\ at\ y=0)};\ 3x^2 + 6x - 12 = 0$$

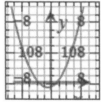

Solve using quadratic equation:

$$x_{1,2} = \frac{-b \pm \sqrt{b^2 - 4ac}}{2a} =$$
$$x = -\sqrt{5} - 1 \text{ or } x = \sqrt{5} - 1$$

Using collected information graph the function, you can verify using 2 or 3 testing points, or in your computer using , for example, Microsoft Mathematics as displayed on left side.

EXAMPLE USING WOLFRAM ALPHA ENGINE.
SOLVE $3x^2 + 6x - 18 = 0$, USE QUADRATIC FORMULA.

Select in step-by-step options "the quadratic formula"

WolframAlpha Step-by-Step Solution ✕

Roots: [Use quadratic formula ▾]   [Hide hints]

STEP 1

Solve for x over the real numbers:

$3x^2 + 6x - 18 = 0$

STEP 2

Hint: Factor constant terms from the left hand side.

$3x^2 + 6x - 18 = 3(x^2 + 2x - 6)$:

$3(x^2 + 2x - 6) = 0$

STEP 3

Hint: Divide both sides by a constant to simplify the equation.

Divide both sides by 3:

$x^2 + 2x - 6 = 0$

STEP 4

Hint: Using the quadratic formula, solve for x.

$x = \dfrac{-2 \pm \sqrt{2^2 - 4(-6)}}{2} = \dfrac{-2 \pm \sqrt{4 + 24}}{2} = \dfrac{-2 \pm \sqrt{28}}{2}$:

$x = \dfrac{-2 + \sqrt{28}}{2}$ or $x = \dfrac{-2 - \sqrt{28}}{2}$

STEP 5

Hint: Simplify radicals.

$\sqrt{28} = \sqrt{4 \times 7} = \sqrt{2^2 \times 7} = 2\sqrt{7}$:

$x = \dfrac{2\sqrt{7} - 2}{2}$ or $x = \dfrac{-2\sqrt{7} - 2}{2}$

STEP 6

> **Hint:** Factor the greatest common divisor
> (gcd) of -2, $2\sqrt{7}$ and 2 from $-2+2\sqrt{7}$.

Factor 2 from $-2+2\sqrt{7}$ giving $2(\sqrt{7}-1)$:

$$x = \frac{1}{2}\,\boxed{2(\sqrt{7}-1)} \ \text{or} \ x = \frac{-2\sqrt{7}-2}{2}$$

STEP 7

> **Hint:** Cancel common terms in the
> numerator and denominator.

$$\frac{2(\sqrt{7}-1)}{2} = \sqrt{7}-1:$$

$$x = \boxed{\sqrt{7}-1} \ \text{or} \ x = \frac{-2\sqrt{7}-2}{2}$$

STEP 8

> **Hint:** Factor the greatest common divisor
> (gcd) of -2, $-2\sqrt{7}$ and 2 from $-2-2\sqrt{7}$.

Factor 2 from $-2-2\sqrt{7}$ giving $2(-\sqrt{7}-1)$:

$$x = \sqrt{7}-1 \ \text{or} \ x = \frac{1}{2}\,\boxed{2(-\sqrt{7}-1)}$$

STEP 9

> **Hint:** Cancel common terms in the
> numerator and denominator.

$$\frac{2(-\sqrt{7}-1)}{2} = -\sqrt{7}-1:$$

> **Answer:**
>
> $$x = \sqrt{7}-1 \ \text{or} \ x = \boxed{-\sqrt{7}-1}$$

3.2. Graph of Polynomial Functions.

The polynomial function in general form can be written as follow:

$$f(x) = a_n x^n + a_{n-1} x^{n-1} + a_{n-2} x^{n-2} + \cdots + a_0$$

End Behavior

The end behavior of the graph of a polynomial function depends of leading term $a_n x^n$ as illustrated below:

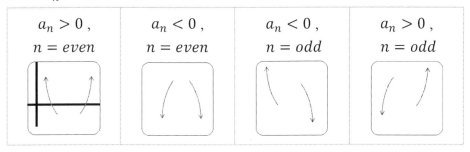

$a_n > 0$, $n = even$	$a_n < 0$, $n = even$	$a_n < 0$, $n = odd$	$a_n > 0$, $n = odd$

Continuous and discontinuous function:

Functions can be continuous and/or discontinuous, as illustrated on the next picture, however, polynomials always are continuous function in the interval (set) of all real number.

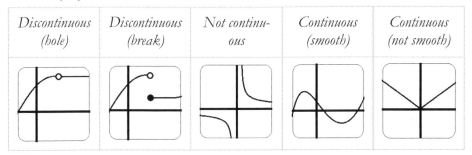

Discontinuous (hole)	*Discontinuous (break)*	*Not continuous*	*Continuous (smooth)*	*Continuous (not smooth)*

Multiplicity:

Multiplicity is an important attribute of the polynomial functions. The multiplicity is referred as per the number of times that the polynomial has identical zero solution. The Multiplicity can be Even or Odd number; for example, If $f(x)$ is a polynomial factored completely

$$f(x) = a_n x^n + a_{n-1} x^{n-1} + \cdots + a_0 = a(x - c_n)(x - c_{n-1}) \ldots (x - c_1)$$

The number of identical solutions in **A** points is/are **Odd number (3 times)**, while in **B** points is/are **Even numbers (2 times)**. With other words, when the multiplicity is even the graph is reflected from the $axis - x$, when the Multiplic-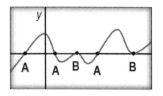
ity is odd the graph crosses the $axis - x$. The following example illustrates the phenomenology:

$$y = (x + 5)^4(x - 3)^3(x - 6)^2(x + 1)$$

Applying zero-product rule for $y = 0$, we get the following solutions: $x = -1$ *or* $x = 6$ *or* $x = 6$ (two times), *or* $x = 3$ *or* $x = 3$ *or* $x = 3$ (three times) *or* (four times) $x = -5$ *or* $x = -5$
or $x = -5$ *or* $x = -5$; In $x = -5$ *and* 6 (**Even** Multiplicity) the graph reflects from $axis$ x. In $x = 3$ (**Odd** Multiplicity) the graph crosses the axis.

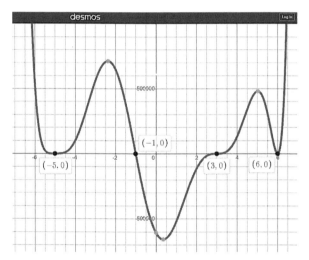

Number of solutions and turning points on the graph

Let's re-define the term "solution" as the zero solution value:

$$f(x) = a_n x^n + a_{n-1}x^{n-1} + a_{n-2}x^{n-2} + \cdots + a_0$$
$$= A(x - c_n)(x - c_{n-1})(x - c_{n-2}) \dots (x - c_1)$$

The solutions are: $x_n = c_n$, $x_{n-1} = c_{n-1}$, $x_{n-2} = c_{n-2}$, ..., $x_0 = c_0$
Considering in the most general form complex solutions: $c = a + bi$, where a *and* b are real coefficients, and $i = \sqrt{-1}$

The solutions are **reals** (interceptions with axis x) when $b = 0$, and **imaginary** (no interception with axis x) when $a = 0$.

It is obviously that the number of factors $(x - c)$ and the number of solutions $c_1, c_2, c_3, \ldots c_n)$ are equal to the degree n of a given polynomial, then, the maximum number of interceptions of the graph (curve) with the $axis - x$ is also the degree n of the given polynomial. If the graph (the curve) cuts the $x - axis$ one time, to cut it again, the curve has to return to the level the $x - axis$; resulting that between two solution exist one turning point. This logic analysis allow us to write the following rule (later on this rule will be confirmed using demonstration that is more advanced).

The degree of the polynomial	n	Maximum number of real solution (cuts the $x - axis$)
The degree minus one	$n - 1$	Number of the turning points

Examples:

Example 1:

Graph: $y = x^3 + x^2 - 12x$

For $x^3 + x^2 - 12x = 0$,

Tree solutions at: $x = 0 \; or \; x = -4 \; or \; x = 3$ and two turning points at:

$x = -\dfrac{1}{3} - (\sqrt{37})/3$ and $= -1/3 + (\sqrt{37})/3$

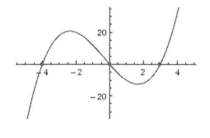

Example 2:

Graph: $y = x^4 - 14x^2 + 45$

Four solutions at:

$x = -3 \; or \; x = 3 \; or$

$x = \sqrt{5} \; or \; x = -\sqrt{5}$ and

three turning points at:

$x = 0, \; +\sqrt{7}, \; and \; -\sqrt{7}$

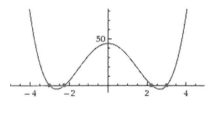

Example 3: Graph: $y = x^4 - x^3 - 8x^2 - 4x - 48$

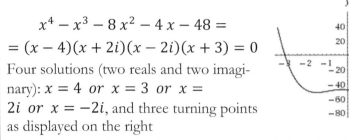
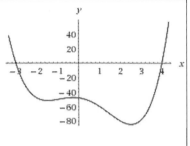

$$x^4 - x^3 - 8x^2 - 4x - 48 =$$
$$= (x - 4)(x + 2i)(x - 2i)(x + 3) = 0$$

Four solutions (two reals and two imaginary): $x = 4 \ or \ x = 3 \ or \ x = 2i \ or \ x = -2i$, and three turning points as displayed on the right

EXAMPLE USING WOLFRAM ALPHA.
LEARN ABOUT FUNCTIONS

Open and learn:

https://www.wolframalpha.com/examples/mathematics/mathematical-functions/

Examples for

Mathematical Functions

In mathematics, a function is defined as a relation, numerical or symbolic, between a set of inputs (known as the function's domain) and a set of potential outputs (the function's codomain). The power of the Wolfram Language enables Wolfram|Alpha to compute properties both for generic functional forms input by the user and for hundreds of known special functions. Use our broad base of functionality to compute properties like periodicity, injectivity, parity, etc. for polynomial, elementary and other special functions.

Domain & Range

Compute the domain and range of a mathematical function.

Compute the domain of a function:

| domain of f(x) = x/(x^2-1) | = |

Compute the range of a function:

| range of e^(-x^2) | = |

Compute domain and range of a function of several variables:

| domain and range of z = x^2 + y^2 | = |

| More examples |

Even & Odd Functions

Determine the parity of a mathematical function.

Determine whether a function is even or odd:

| what is the parity of sin(x) | = |

Injectivity & Surjectivity

Determine the injectivity and surjectivity of a mathematical function.

Determine whether a given function is injective:

| is y=x^3+x a one-to-one function? | = |

Determine whether a given function is surjective:

| is x^2-x surjective? | = |

| More examples |

Periodic Functions

Compute the period of a periodic function.

Compute the period of a periodic function:

| period y=sin(x)*cos(3x) | = |

Find periods of a function of several variables:

| period sin(x + y^2 - 3z) | = |

RELATED EXAMPLES

- Calculus & Analysis
- Continued Fractions
- Differential Equations
- Polynomials
- Rational Functions

Continuity

Determine the continuity of a mathematical function.

Determine whether a function is continuous:

| is sin(x-1.1)/(x-1.1)+heaviside(x) continuous | = |

Locate discontinuities of a function:

| discontinuities (x^3+5)/(x^3+3x^2-4x-12) | = |

| More examples |

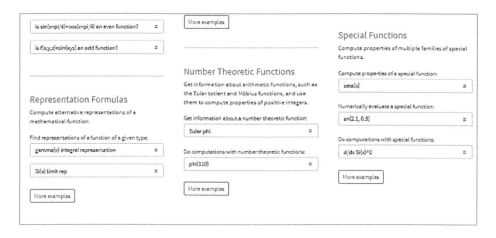

EXAMPLE USING MICROSOFT MATHEMATICS.
LEARN ABOUT FUNCTIONS, SOLVING/GRAPHING, IDENTIFYING END
CHARACTER, NUMBER OF SOLUTIONS, TURNING POINTS, FACTOR AND SOLVE
TO FIND THE SOLUTIONS/INTERCEPTS.

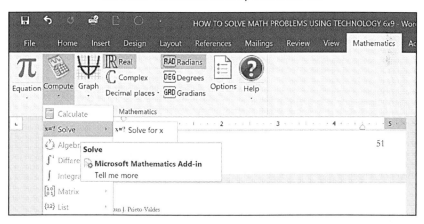

1. $y = x^3 + x^2 - 12x$

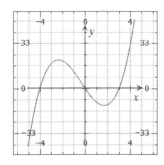

END CHARACTER: Opens up on the right and down on the left because leading coefficient is a positive (+1) odd number (3).

SOLUTIONS: The function has tree possible solutions and two turning points:

$$y = x^3 + x^2 - 12x == x(x^2 + x - 12)$$
$$= x(x + 4)(x - 3) = 0$$

Solutions: $x_1 = 0,\quad x_2 = -4,\quad x_3 = 3$ which are the $x_{intercepts}$ and $y_{intercept}$ will be located at $x = 0$, *resulting* $y = 0$; $(0,0) = y_{int}$

2. $y = -x^3 - 3x^2 + 4x + 12$

END CHARACTER: Opens down on the right and up on the left because leading coefficient is a negative (-1) odd number (3).

SOLUTIONS: The function has tree possible solutions and two turning points. Factor by grouping:

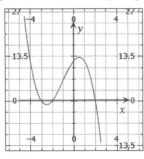

$$y = -x^2(x + 3) + 4(x + 3)$$
$$= (x + 3)(4 - x^2) =$$
$$= (x + 3)(2 - x)(2 + x) = 0$$

So: $x_1 = -3,\quad x_2 = -2,\quad x_3 = 2$ are the solutions ($x_{intercepts}$)

and $y_{intercept}$ is located at $x = 0,\ y = 12$

3. $y = x^4 - 25x^2 + 144$

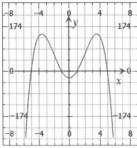

END CHARACTER: Opens up on the right and on the left because leading coefficient is a positive (+1) even number (4).

SOLUTIONS: The function has four possible solutions and tree turning points. Factor four degree equation like a quadratic::

$$y = (x^2 - 16)(x^2 - 9) =$$
$$= (x - 4)(x + 4)(x - 3)(x + 3) = 0$$

The solutions are $x_{intercepts}$: $x_1 = 4,\quad x_2 = -4,\quad x_3 = 3,\quad x_4 = -3$

at $x = 0,\ y = 144$, so, $y_{intercept} = (0, 144)$

3.3. The Real Zeros of a Polynomial.

3.3.1. Factor Theorem:

Let $f(x)$ be a polynomial function. Then $(x - c)$ is a factor of $f(x)$ if and only if $f(c) = 0$

58

Let's consider $n - degree$ completely factorable polynomial,

where $a_n \neq 0 \ and \ a_0 \neq 0$,

$$f(x) = a_n x^n + a_{n-1} x^{n-1} + a_{n-2} x^{n-2} + \cdots + a_0$$

Then: $f(x) = A(x - c_n)(x - c_{n-1})(x - c_{n-2}) \ldots (x - c_1)$

Proof:

The solutions will be:: $x_n = c_n, \ x_{n-1} = c_{n-1}, \ x_{n-2} = c_{n-2}, \ \ldots, \ x_1 = c_1$

If replacing the solution value in a corresponding factor (binomial),

$f(x)$ becomes zero as $c_n - c_n = 0$, as well as for any other solution

$$f(x) = A(c_n - c_n)(x - c_{n-1})(x - c_{n-2}) \ldots (x - c_1) = 0$$

Equivalencies/evidences:

1. Equivalencies: c is a zero of $f(x)$
2. $x = c$ is a solution of the equation $f(x) = 0$
3. $(x - c)$ is a factor of $f(x)$
4. c is an $x - intercept$ of the graph of $f(x)$

Example:

$$f(x) = x^4 - x^3 - 29 x^2 + 9 x + 180 = (x - 5)(x - 3)(x + 3)(x + 4)$$

$f(x) = x^4 - x^3 - 29 x^2 + 9 x + 180 = 0$, the solutions are: $x = -3 \ or \ x = 3 \ or \ x = -4 \ or \ x = 5$

Accordingly with the factor theorem:

$$f(-3) = (-3)^4 - (-3)^3 - 29 (-3)^2 + 9 (-3) + 180 = 0$$
$$f(3) = (3)^4 - (3)^3 - 29 (3)^2 + 9 (3) + 180 = 0$$
$$f(-4) = (-4)^4 - (-4)^3 - 29 (-4)^2 + 9 (-4) + 180 = 0$$
$$f(5) = (5)^4 - (5)^3 - 29 (5)^2 + 9 (5) + 180 = 0$$

3.3.2.   Remainder Theorem:

Let $f(x)$ be a polynomial function which is not completely factorable. If $f(x)$ is divided by $(x - c)$, in this case

$$c - any \ number, not \ a \ zero \ solution,$$

then the remainder is $f(c)$.

Les consider that, dividing $f(x)$ by $q(x)$ gives $h(x) +$ a remainder

In other words (formulation), as follow:

$$Dividend = (Quotient)(Divisor) + Remainder$$

$$\frac{f(x)}{q(x)} = h(x) + \frac{r(x)}{q(x)} \quad or \quad f(x) = h(x)q(x) + r(x)$$

Where: $f(x)$ is the dividend, $q(x)$ is the divisor, $h(x)$ is the quotient and $r(x)$ the remainder. To factor a polynomial, we try to get $q(x)$ in a form of first degree polynomial (binomial):

$$f(x) = (x - c)h(x) + r(x),$$

where c is a real number. If $r(x) = 0$ the polynomial is perfectly divisible by $q(x)$, and $q(x) = (x - c)$ represent a zero of $f(x)$: we say $c -$ *is a solution.* Also we say $f(x)$ is factored completely. Based on previous analysis we can enunciate:

If $f(x)$ is divided by $(x - c)$, them the remaining is $f(c)$. In this case $x = c$ is not a zero solution.

And $(x - c)$ is a factor of $f(x)$ if and only if and $f(c) = 0$, in this case, $x = c$ is a zero solution.

3.3.3.   Rational Zeros Theorem

Let $f(x)$ be a polynomial $n - degree$ completely factorable (where $a_n \neq 0 \; and \; a_0 \neq 0$) of the form:

$$f(x) = a_n x^n + a_{n-1}x^{n-1} + a_{n-2}x^{n-2} + \cdots + a_0$$
$$f(x) = A(x - c_n)(x - c_{n-1})(x - c_{n-2}) \ldots (x - c_1)$$

Where each a coefficient is an integer.

If $\pm\frac{p}{q}$ in lowest term, is a rational zero of $f(x)$, then p must be a factor of a_0 and q must be a factor of a_n.

Examples:

Let's consider $a_n = 1$. In this case p is a possible factor of a_0, then p is a solution.

Degree	Solutions (possible factor of $\pm c_0$)	Factors	Polynomial Expression	c_0
2	$x = 4$, $x = -2$	$(x-4)(x+2)$	$x^2 - 2x - 8$	8
3	$x = -3, -1,$ and 3	$(x+3)(x+1)(x-3)$	$x^3 + x^2 - 9x - 9$	9
4	$-4, -3, 0, 3,$ and 5	$(x+4)(x+3)(x-3)(x-5)$	$x^4 - x^3 - 29x^2 + 9x + 180$	180
5	$-2, -1, 2, 3$ and 1	$(x+2)(x+1)(x-2)(x-3)(x-1)$	$x^5 - 9x^4 + 7x^3 + 57x^2 - 44x - 84$	84

More Examples:

Considering $a_n - $ **any number**. In this case: p is a possible factor of a_0, while q is a possible factor of a_n; then, some possible quotients of $\pm \frac{p}{q}$ will be the solutions $c_n \dots c_1$,

Example 1:

$f(x) = x^3 - 4x^2 - 44x + 96$, (Graph on the right)

Factors of $a_0 = 96$ are: $\pm 1, \pm 2, \pm 4, \pm 6, \pm 8, \pm 12, \pm 16, \pm 32$

Factors of $a_n = 1$ are: ± 1

So, possible Zeros are: $\dfrac{Factors\ of\ a_0}{Factors\ of\ a_n} =$

$$= \pm\frac{1}{1}, \pm\frac{2}{1}, \pm\frac{4}{1}, \pm\frac{6}{1}, \pm\frac{8}{1}, \pm\frac{12}{1}, \pm\frac{16}{1}, \pm\frac{32}{1}$$

Because third degree polynomial, at least 3 of them have to be solutions. If testing all these numbers, we can discover that

$$r(2) = r(-6) = r(8) = 0$$

and equivalently $f(2) = f(-6) = f(8) = 0$

Checking, for $x = 8$: $\qquad f(8) = 8^3 - 4\times 8^2 - 44\times 8 + 960 = 0$

And $f(x)$ is perfectly divisible by $(x - 8)$. So: $\frac{f(x)}{x-8} = (x^2 + 4x - 12)$

The remainder are equal to zero at $x = 8$ (solid points). The same situation for $(x - 2)$ and $(x + 6)$; as well as $f(-6)$ and $f(2)$, both equal to zero.

They also are real solution of the polynomial

So: $(x - 8)(x - 2)(x + 6)$ and $x = 8$, $x = 2$, and $x = -6$

are factors of the polynomial

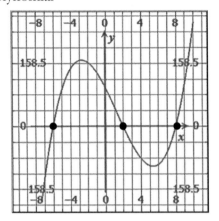

Example 2:

$$y = 4x^3 - 4x^2 - 88x + 160$$

Let's consider that this polynomial can be factored completely as follow:

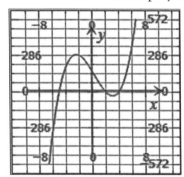

$$f(x) = A(x - c_1)(x - c_2)(x - c_3)$$

The factors of a_0 and a_n are a quotient of

$$\pm \frac{All\ posible\ factors\ of\ 160}{All\ posible\ factors\ of\ 4}$$

$Factors\ of\ 160 = \pm(1, 2, 4, 8, 10, etc\ ...)$

$Factors\ of\ 4 = \pm(1, 2, 4)$;

after dividing all possible combination, three of them satisfy the remainder theorem

$f(c) = 0$, they are: $c_{1,2,3} = \frac{2}{1}, \frac{4}{1}$ or $\frac{8}{2}$, and $-\frac{10}{2}$. Then, our polynomial can be written as; $y = 4(x - 4)(x - 2)(x + 5)$

and the solutions are: 2, 4, and 5.

3.3.4.   Descartes' Rule of Signs

Probably, the most tedious moment in previously described exercises is the correct selection of the factors $\frac{p}{q}$, especialy when the numeric value of the coefficients a_n and a_0 are big numbers having many factors. Descartes

Rule is a helpful rule in eliminating candidates from lengthy list of possible rational roots. To describe this rule, we need the concept of variation in sing, as follow:

If $f(x)$ is a polynomial with real coefficients, written in descending order of x , then a variation in sign occurs whenever adjacent coefficients have opposite signs. The rule can be synthesized as follow:

1. The number of positive real zeros of $f(x)$ either is equal to the number of variation in sign in $f(x)$ or is less than by an even whole number.

2. The number of negative real zeros of $f(x)$ either is equal to the number of variations in sign in $f(-x)$ or is less than by an even whole number.

Example 1:

$$f(x) = x^4 - x^3 - 29x^2 + 9x + 180$$

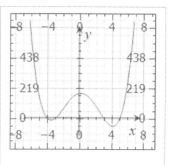

Two sign variation when using $e\,x$. Means that two solution will be positive.

$$f(-x) = x^4 + x^3 - 29x^2 - 9x + 180$$

And two negative solution as two times the sign change when using $negative\ x$

Example **2:**

$$f(x) = 3x^6 + 4x^5 + 3x^3 - x^2 + x - 8$$

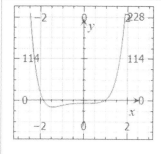

Three times the sign varieties, so could be 3 or $(3 - 2) = 1$ positive $x\ solutions$.

$$f(-x) = 3x^6 - 4x^5 - 3x^3 - x^2 - x - 8$$

Only one change, then we have only one negative solution.

In the next page a model example and full analysis/calculation.

Model Example: Finding the zeroes of a polynomial.

Given $f(x) = 2x^5 - 5x^4 + x^3 + x^2 - x + 6$

1. **List all possible zeroes (use Rational Zeros Theorem)** Note that $a_n = 2$ *and* $a_0 = 6$.

   Then, the factors of 2 and 6 are: $\{\pm 1 \ and \ \pm 2\}$ and $\{\pm 1, \pm 2, \pm 3 \ and \ \pm 6\}$.

   The possible rational zeros for $f(x)$ are: $\left\{\pm 1, \pm \frac{1}{2}, \pm \frac{3}{2} \pm 2, \pm 3, \pm 6\right\}$.

2. **Applying Descartes' Rule.** Organize the work using a Table for listing **all possible zeroes** after counting the changes in signs for $f(x)$ *and* $f(-x)$.

$$f(x) = 2x^5 - 5x^4 + x^3 + x^2 - x + 6 \ \text{\{four sing changes\}}$$
$$f(x) = -2x^5 - 5x^4 - x^3 + x^2 + x + 6 \ \text{\{one sign change\}}$$

Positive (P)	Negative (N)	Real Zeroes (P+N)	Complex Zeroes
4	1	5	0
$4 - 2 = 2$	1	3	2
$4 - 4 = 0$	1	1	4

3. Test the possible values using remainder theorem $(f(c) = 0)$.
   First Test: $f(x) = 2(1)^5 - 5(1)^4 + (1)^3 + x(1)^2 - (1) + 6 \neq 0$
   Second: $f(x) = 2(-1)^5 - 5(-1)^4 + (-1)^3 + (-1)^2 - (-1) + 6 = 0$
   we're lucky, in the second attempt we found solution $(x = -1)$. Then $(x + 1)$ is a factor of the given polynomial, and because it is a factor, given polynomial is divisible by $(x + 1)$, and will not be a remainder.

4. Divide. Let's divide using synthetic division to facilitate the operation:

   Remember remainder theorem $\frac{f(x)}{q(x)} = h(x) + \frac{r(x)}{q(x)}$ or $f(x) = h(x)q(x) + r(x)$, where $r(x) = 0$

Use divisor $\{-1\}$	-1 / 2 -5 1 1 -1	Coefficients of $f(x)$
	6	
	-2 7 -8 7 -	
	6	
	2 -7 8 -7 6	Coefficients of $q(x)$
	0	

5. $q(x)$ is not easy factorable, so we need to divide one more time using any other solution. Since there is only one negative solution $(x = -1)$, we have to continue searching for another possible solution but positive.

Third Test: $f(x) = 2(2)^5 - 5(2)^4 + (2)^3 + (2)^2 - (2) + 6 = 0$

One more time we are lucky, in the third attempt we found another solution $(x = 2)$. Then $(x - 2)$ is a factor of the given polynomial, and because it is a factor, given polynomial is divisible by $(x - 2)$, and will not be a remainder.

Use divisor {2}	2 /	2	-7	8	-7	6	Coefficients of $f(x)$
			4	-6	-4	-6	
		2	-3	2	-3	0	Coefficients of $q(x)$

6. Now we can write in partially factored form:
$$f(x) = (x + 1)(x - 2)(2x^3 - 3x^2 + 2x - 3)$$
and continue factoring by grouping:
$$f(x) = (x + 1)(x - 2)\big(x^2(2x - 3) + (2x - 3)\big)$$
$$= (x + 1)(x - 2)(2x - 3)(x^2 + 1) =$$

$$= (x + 1)(x - 2)(2x - 3)(x + i)(x - i)$$

Previous example illustrates very well the end behavior of the graph for odd function, and how to use Rational Zeros, Factor and Remainder theorems to factor any polynomial. Interesting that the second Table line in Descartes' Rule analysis (point 2 above) was a good prediction of existing five (5) solutions, three reals and two complexes:

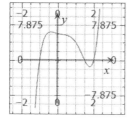

$$x = -1 \quad x = 2 \quad x = \frac{3}{2} \quad x = -i \quad \text{and } x = +i$$

We can visualize four turning points on the graph. Note that complex solution are conjugates. This will be one more challenge to discus in the next topic.

EXAMPLE USING WOLFRAM ALPHA ENGINE.
FACTOR AND GRAPH. $y = 2x^5 - 19x^4 + 58x^3 - 67x^2 + 56x - 48$.

Check the step-by-step analysis and compare the solution procedure with previous example solved by traditional method.

STEP 1

Factor the following:
$$2x^5 - 5x^4 + x^3 + x^2 - x + 6$$

STEP 2

> **Hint:** Find all linear factors of $2x^5 - 5x^4 + x^3 + x^2 - x + 6$ via the rational root theorem. Do this by finding rational roots. The candidates are $x = \pm\dfrac{p}{q}$ for all p that are divisors of the constant term 6 and for all q that are divisors of the leading coefficient 2.

The possible rational roots of $2x^5 - 5x^4 + x^3 + x^2 - x + 6$ are
$x = \pm\dfrac{1}{2}, x = \pm\dfrac{3}{2}, x = \pm1, x = \pm2, x = \pm3, x = \pm6$. Of these,
$x = \dfrac{3}{2}, x = -1$ and $x = 2$ are roots. This gives $2x - 3$, $x + 1$ and $x - 2$ as all linear
factors:

$$\frac{(2x - 3)(x + 1)(x - 2)\left(2x^5 - 5x^4 + x^3 + x^2 - x + 6\right)}{(2x - 3)(x + 1)(x - 2)}$$

STEP 3

> **Hint:** Divide $x - 2$ into $2x^5 - 5x^4 + x^3 + x^2 - x + 6$.

$$
\begin{array}{r}
2x^4 - x^3 - x^2 - x - 3 \\
x - 2 \,\overline{\big)\, 2x^5 - 5x^4 + x^3 + x^2 - x + 6} \\
\underline{2x^5 - 4x^4} \\
-x^4 + x^3 \\
\underline{-x^4 + 2x^3} \\
-x^3 + x^2 \\
\underline{-x^3 + 2x^2} \\
-x^2 - x \\
\underline{-x^2 + 2x} \\
-3x + 6 \\
\underline{-3x + 6} \\
0
\end{array}
$$

$$\frac{2x^4 - x^3 - x^2 - x - 3}{(x + 1)(2x - 3)} \; (2x - 3)(x + 1)(x - 2)$$

Juan J. Prieto-Valdes

STEP 4

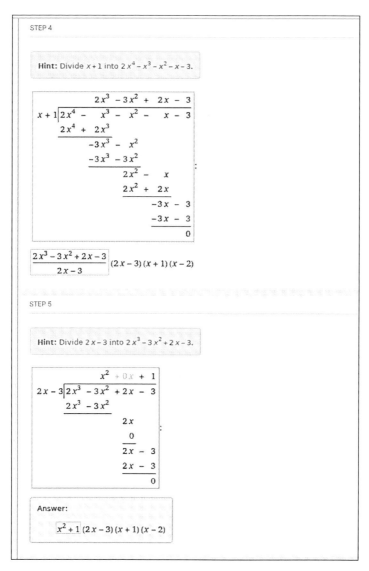

Hint: Divide $x + 1$ into $2x^4 - x^3 - x^2 - x - 3$.

$$2x^3 - 3x^2 + 2x - 3$$
$$x + 1 \overline{)\, 2x^4 - x^3 - x^2 - x - 3}$$
$$\underline{2x^4 + 2x^3}$$
$$-3x^3 - x^2$$
$$\underline{-3x^3 - 3x^2}$$
$$2x^2 - x$$
$$\underline{2x^2 + 2x}$$
$$-3x - 3$$
$$\underline{-3x - 3}$$
$$0$$

$$\frac{2x^3 - 3x^2 + 2x - 3}{2x - 3} \quad (2x - 3)(x + 1)(x - 2)$$

STEP 5

Hint: Divide $2x - 3$ into $2x^3 - 3x^2 + 2x - 3$.

$$x^2 + 0x + 1$$
$$2x - 3 \overline{)\, 2x^3 - 3x^2 + 2x - 3}$$
$$\underline{2x^3 - 3x^2}$$
$$2x$$
$$0$$
$$\underline{}$$
$$2x - 3$$
$$2x - 3$$
$$0$$

Answer:

$$x^2 + 1 \,(2x - 3)(x + 1)(x - 2)$$

Plots:

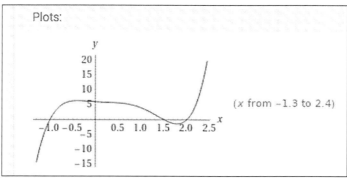

(x from -1.3 to 2.4)

67

3.4. Complex Zeros and the Fundamental Theorem of Algebra

1. Any factorable polynomial with complex coefficients has at least one complex zero.

$$f(x) = a_n x^n + a_{n-1} x^{n-1} + a_{n-2} x^{n-2} + \cdots + a_0$$

2. If $f(x)$ is a polynomial of degree $n \neq 1$, then exist complex numbers $A, c_1, c_2, \ldots, c_0$, such that:

$$f(x) = A(x - c_n)(x - c_{n-1})(x - c_{n-2}) \ldots (x - c_0).$$

Because any real number is also a complex number, the previous Fundamental Theorem of Algebra (1) and the Complete Factorization Theorem (2) also applies to polynomials with real coefficients.

Example 1.

Simple factorization by grouping. Three solutions: one real and two complex-imaginary.

$$f(x) = x^3 - 2x^2 + 2x - 4 = x^2(x - 2) + 2(x - 2) =$$
$$= (x - 2)(x^2 + 2) = (x - 2)(x - \sqrt{2}\,i)(x + \sqrt{2}\,i)$$

Example 2.

Not easy factorization. Apply Factor and Remainder Theorem and quadratic formula.

$$f(x) = x^4 - 3x^3 - 12x^2 + 54x - 40$$

Factors of $40 = \pm 1, \pm 2, \pm 4, \pm 8, etc \ldots$

Let's search for (at least) two roots.

$$f(-1) \neq 0; \quad f(1) = 0 \text{ (Bravo !)};$$
$$f(-2) \neq 0; \quad f(2) \neq 0; \quad f(-4) = 0 \text{ (}Bravo\text{ !); etc}$$

Synthetic division:

Use divisor $\{-4\}$	-4 /	1	-3	-12	54	-40	Coefficients $f(x)$
			-4	28	-64	40	
		1	-7	16	-10	0	Coefficients $q(x)$

$$f(x) = x^4 - 3x^3 - 12x^2 + 54x - 40 =$$
$$= (x+4)(x^3 - 7x^2 + 16x - 10)$$

Continue the procedure, Now divide by (x-1) factor

Use divisor $\{1\}$	1 /	1	-7	16	-10	Coefficients $f(x)$
			1	-6	10	
		1	-6	10	0	Coefficients $q(x)$

$$f(x) = x^4 - 3x^3 - 12x^2 + 54x - 40 =$$
$$= (x+4)(x^3 - 7x^2 + 16x - 10) = (x+4)(x-1)(x^2 - 6x + 10)$$

The remainder trinomial can be solved using quadratic formula:

$$x = \frac{-b \pm \sqrt{b^2 - 4ac}}{2a} = \frac{-6 \pm \sqrt{36 - 4(1)(10)}}{2(1)} = \frac{6 \pm \sqrt{-4}}{2} = 3 \pm i$$

Final factorization: $f(x) = (x - 3 - i)(x - 3 + i)(x + 4)(x - 1)$

EXAMPLE: COMPLETE FACTORIZATION IN PREVIOUS EXAMPLE.
$$y = 2X^5 - 19X^4 + 58X^3 - 67X^2 + 56X - 48 .$$

Check the step-by-step analysis and complete the previous example to find all solutions (real and imaginary), solve $(x^2 - 6x + 10)$:

STEP 1

Solve for x:
$$2x^5 - 19x^4 + 58x^3 - 67x^2 + 56x - 48 = 0$$

STEP 2

Hint: Factor the left hand side.

The left hand side factors into a product with three terms:
$$(x - 4)^2 (2x - 3)(x^2 + 1) = 0$$

STEP 3

Hint: Find the roots of each term in the product separately.

Split into three equations:
$$(x - 4)^2 = 0 \text{ or } 2x - 3 = 0 \text{ or } x^2 + 1 = 0$$

STEP 4

> **Hint:** Look at the first equation: Write the quadratic polynomial on the left hand side in standard form.

Expand out terms of the left hand side:

$x^2 - 8x + 16 = 0$ or $2x - 3 = 0$ or $x^2 + 1 = 0$

STEP 5

> **Hint:** Using the quadratic formula, solve for x.

$$x = \frac{8 \pm \sqrt{(-8)^2 - 4 \times 16}}{2} = \frac{8 \pm \sqrt{64 - 64}}{2} = \frac{8 \pm \sqrt{0}}{2} = \frac{8 \pm 0}{2} = 4 \pm 0:$$

$x = 4$ or $x = 4$ or $2x - 3 = 0$ or $x^2 + 1 = 0$

STEP 6

> **Hint:** Look at the third equation: Isolate terms with x to the left hand side.

Add 3 to both sides:

$x = 4$ or $x = 4$ or $2x = 3$ or $x^2 + 1 = 0$

STEP 7

> **Hint:** Solve for x.

Divide both sides by 2:

$x = 4$ or $x = 4$ or $x = \dfrac{3}{2}$ or $x^2 + 1 = 0$

STEP 8

> **Hint:** Look at the fourth equation: Using the quadratic formula, solve for x.

$$x = \frac{0 \pm \sqrt{0^2 - 4}}{2} = \frac{\pm \sqrt{-4}}{2}:$$

$x = 4$ or $x = 4$ or $x = \dfrac{3}{2}$ or $x = \dfrac{\sqrt{-4}}{2}$ or $x = \dfrac{-\sqrt{-4}}{2}$

STEP 9

Hint: Express $\sqrt{-4}$ in terms of i.

$\sqrt{-4} = \sqrt{-1}\sqrt{4} = i\sqrt{4}$:

$x = 4$ or $x = 4$ or $x = \dfrac{3}{2}$ or $x = \dfrac{i\sqrt{4}}{2}$ or $x = \dfrac{-i\sqrt{4}}{2}$

STEP 10

Hint: Simplify radicals.

$\sqrt{4} = \sqrt{2^2} = 2$:

$x = 4$ or $x = 4$ or $x = \dfrac{3}{2}$ or $x = \dfrac{i\times 2}{2}$ or $x = \dfrac{-i\times 2}{2}$

STEP 11

Hint: Look at the fourth equation: Cancel common terms in the numerator and denominator.

$\dfrac{i\times 2}{2} = i$:

$x = 4$ or $x = 4$ or $x = \dfrac{3}{2}$ or $x = i$ or $x = \dfrac{-2i}{2}$

STEP 12

Hint: Cancel common terms in the numerator and denominator.

$\dfrac{-i\times 2}{2} = -i$:

$x = 4$ or $x = 4$ or $x = \dfrac{3}{2}$ or $x = i$ or $x = -i$

Now get the final solution and graph:

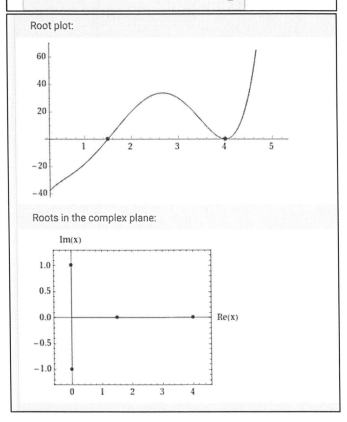

Hint: Remove duplicate solutions.

There is one duplicate solution:

Answer:
$$x = 4 \text{ or } x = -i \text{ or } x = i \text{ or } x = \frac{3}{2}$$

Root plot:

Roots in the complex plane:

3.4.1. Complex Zeros Come in Conjugate Pairs

Let's consider a polynomial
$$f(x) = a_n x^n + a_{n-1} x^{n-1} + a_{n-2} x^{n-2} + \cdots + a_0$$
$a + bi$ is a solution only and only if $a - bi$ is also a solution.

Proof:
$$f(x) = a_n(a + bi)^n + a_{n-1}x(a + bi)^{n-1} + a_{n-2}(a + bi)^{n-2} + \cdots + a_0$$

$$f(x) = a_n(a - bi)^n + a_{n-1}(a - bi)^{n-1} + a_{n-2}(a - bi)^{n-2} + \cdots + a_0$$

Using the fact that the sum of complex conjugates is the sum of conjugates and the product is the product of conjugates we can demonstrate that both solutions are correct, however, to facilitate the understanding let's analyze a simple numeric examples:

1. $x^2 - 2x + 2 =$ $= (x - 1 + i)(x - 1 - i)$	5. $x^2 + 2x + 2 =$ $= (x + 1 + i)(x + 1 - i)$
2. $x^2 - 4x + 5 =$ $= (x - 2 + i)(x - 2 - i)$	6. $x^2 + 4x + 5 =$ $= (x + 2 + i)(x + 2 - i)$
3. $x^2 - 6x + 10 =$ $= (x - 3 + i)(x - 3 - i)$	7. $x^2 + 6x + 10 =$ $= (x + 3 + i)(x + 3 - i)$
4. $x^2 - 8x + 17 =$ $= (x - 4 + i)(x - 4 - i)$	8. $x^2 + 8x + 17 =$ $= (x + 4 + i)(x + 4 - i)$

Previous analysis serves to demonstrate a special product rule for conjugates

$$x^2 - 2ax + (a^2 + b^2) = [x - (a + bi)][x - (a - bi)]$$

Where a and b are $\mathbb{R}$, different than cero $(\neq 0)$, The coefficient b has to be positive $(b \neq 0)$ to satisfy the condition of the existence of conjugates. Also the discriminant of the quadratic formula has to be negative to satisfy the imaginary solution $(B^2 - 4AC < 0)$. The term C on the quadratic equation/formula is equivalently to our $(a^2 + b^2)$ term. For real; solutions $(b = 0)$; in this case previous trinomial becomes a perfect square trinomial with two identical solutions coming from the square of binomial

$$(x + a)^2 \ or \ (x - a)^2.$$

Example:

Factor $f(x) = 2x^5 + 17x^4 + 49x^3 + 38x^2 - 46x - 60$

Factors of 2 are: ± 1; ± 2. Factors of 60 are:

± 1; ± 2; ± 3; ± 4; ± 5; ± 6; etc

The possible root are: ± 1; $\pm \frac{3}{2}$; ± 2; ± 3; etc. Let's try with the first four root, if needed later we can recalculate some more roots.

$$f(1) = 0; \ (it \ works, Bravo!);$$

$f(-1) \neq 0; \ f(2) = 0 \ (Bravo!); f(-2) \neq 0; \ f\left(-\frac{3}{2}\right) = 0 \ (Bravo!)$

We found 3 roots. If needed we can calculate more.

Use divisor {1}	1 /	2	17	49	38	-46	-60	$(x - 1)$
			2	19	68	106	60	
Use divisor {-2}	-2/	2	19	68	106	60	0	$(x + 2)$
			-4	-30	-76	-60		
Use divisor {-3/2 }	$-\frac{3}{2}$ /	2	15	38	30	0		$(2x + 3)$
			$-\frac{6}{2}$	$-\frac{36}{2}$	$-\frac{60}{2}$			
		2	12	20	0			$(2x^2 + 12x + 20)$

$(2x^2 + 12x + 10)$ can be factored using the product rule for conjugates (Example #7 in topic 3.4.1.)

Finally we can write:

$$f(x) = 2(x^2 + 6x + 10)(x - 1)(x + 2)(2x + 3)$$
$$= 2(x + 3 + i)(x + 3 - i)(x - 1)(x + 2)(2x + 3)$$

The solutions are: $x = -3 - i.\ x = -3 + i,\ x = 1,\ x = -2,\ x = -\frac{2}{3}.$

EXAMPLE USING WOLFRAM ALPHA ENGINE.
FACTOR PREVIOUS EXAMPLE COMPLETELY

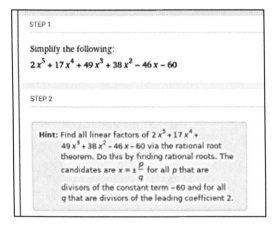

STEP 1

Simplify the following:
$2x^5 + 17x^4 + 49x^3 + 38x^2 - 46x - 60$

STEP 2

Hint: Find all linear factors of $2x^5 + 17x^4 + 49x^3 + 38x^2 - 46x - 60$ via the rational root theorem. Do this by finding rational roots. The candidates are $x = \pm\frac{p}{q}$ for all p that are divisors of the constant term -60 and for all q that are divisors of the leading coefficient 2.

The possible rational roots of $2x^5 + 17x^4 + 49x^3 + 38x^2 - 46x - 60$ are

$x = \pm\dfrac{1}{2}, x = \pm\dfrac{3}{2}, x = \pm\dfrac{5}{2}, x = \pm\dfrac{15}{2}, x = \pm 1, x = \pm 2, x = \pm 3, x = \pm 4, x = \pm 5,$

$x = \pm 6, x = \pm 10, x = \pm 12, x = \pm 15, x = \pm 20, x = \pm 30, x = \pm 60.$ Of these,

$x = -\dfrac{3}{2}, x = 1$ and $x = -2$ are roots. This gives $2x + 3, x - 1$ and $x + 2$ as all

linear factors:

$$\frac{(2x+3)(x-1)(x+2)\left(2x^5 + 17x^4 + 49x^3 + 38x^2 - 46x - 60\right)}{(2x+3)(x-1)(x+2)}$$

STEP 3

Hint: Divide $x - 1$ into $2x^5 + 17$
$x^4 + 49x^3 + 38x^2 - 46x - 60.$

$$
\begin{array}{r}
2x^4 + 19x^3 + 68x^2 + 106x + 60 \\
x-1\overline{\smash{\big)}\,2x^5 + 17x^4 + 49x^3 + 38x^2 - 46x - 60} \\
\underline{2x^5 - 2x^4} \\
19x^4 + 49x^3 \\
\underline{19x^4 - 19x^3} \\
68x^3 + 38x^2 \\
\underline{68x^3 - 68x^2} \\
106x^2 - 46x \\
\underline{106x^2 - 106x} \\
60x - 60 \\
\underline{60x - 60} \\
0
\end{array}
$$

$$\frac{2x^4 + 19x^3 + 68x^2 + 106x + 60}{(x+2)(2x+3)}(2x+3)(x-1)(x+2)$$

STEP 4

Hint: Divide $x + 2$ into $2x^4 + 19x^3 + 68x^2 + 106x + 60.$

$$
\begin{array}{r}
2x^3 + 15x^2 + 38x + 30 \\
x+2\overline{\smash{\big)}\,2x^4 + 19x^3 + 68x^2 + 106x + 60} \\
\underline{2x^4 + 4x^3} \\
15x^3 + 68x^2 \\
\underline{15x^3 + 30x^2} \\
38x^2 + 106x \\
\underline{38x^2 + 76x} \\
30x + 60 \\
\underline{30x + 60} \\
0
\end{array}
$$

$$\frac{2x^3 + 15x^2 + 38x + 30}{2x+3}(2x+3)(x-1)(x+2)$$

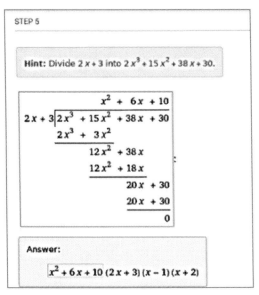

Continue factoring to find complex roots. You can select completing the square or quadratic formula:

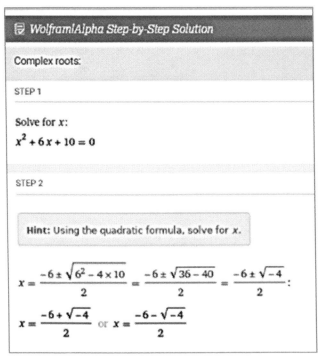

STEP 3

Hint: Express $\sqrt{-4}$ in terms of i.

$$\sqrt{-4} = \sqrt{-1}\sqrt{4} = i\sqrt{4}:$$

$$x = \frac{-6 + i\sqrt{4}}{2} \text{ or } x = \frac{-6 - i\sqrt{4}}{2}$$

STEP 4

Hint: Simplify radicals.

$$\sqrt{4} = \sqrt{2^2} = 2:$$

$$x = \frac{-6 + i \times 2}{2} \text{ or } x = \frac{-6 - i \times 2}{2}$$

STEP 5

Hint: Factor the greatest common divisor (gcd) of -6, $2i$ and 2 from $-6 + 2i$.

Factor 2 from $-6 + 2i$ giving $-6 + 2i$:

$$x = \frac{1}{2}\boxed{-6 + 2i} \text{ or } x = \frac{-6 - 2i}{2}$$

STEP 6

Hint: Cancel common terms in the numerator and denominator.

$$\frac{-6 + 2i}{2} = -3 + i:$$

$$x = 1i - 3 \text{ or } x = \frac{-6 - 2i}{2}$$

STEP 7

Hint: Factor the greatest common divisor (gcd) of $-6, -2i$ and 2 from $-6-2i$.

Factor 2 from $-6-2i$ giving $-6-2i$:

$$x = -3+i \text{ or } x = \frac{1}{2}\boxed{-6-2i}$$

STEP 8

Hint: Cancel common terms in the numerator and denominator.

$$\frac{-6-2i}{2} = -3-i:$$

Answer:

$$x = -3+i \text{ or } x = \boxed{-3-i}$$

Steps for Finding the Real Zeros of a Polynomial Function.

1. Determine the end behavior of the graph as per leading term (coefficient) value
2. Determine the y-intercept by evaluating $f(0)$
3. Determine real zeros, evaluating (solving) the equation at y=0, apply Factor and Remainder Theorems if needed, also if needed use long division or synthetic division as you feel more comfortable, and
4. Determine their Multiplicity and the number of possible real and complex solution in a negative and positive side using Descartes Rule.
5. Plot all intercepts with x and y axis and sketch the graph character as per zeros multiplicity that you have determined before.
6. Use Symmetry characteristics and some testing points (if needed) to construct the graph.

3.5. Property and Graph of Rational Functions.

A function $f(x)$ is called a rational function if and only if it can be written in the form of

$$R(x) = \frac{P(x)}{Q(x)},$$

where P and Q are polynomials in x and Q never equal to zero.

The Domain of $f(x)$ is the set of all points x for which the denominator $Q(x)$ is not zero, assuming P and Q have no common factors. The values of x that make the denominator equal to zero, are "prohibit", as the rational function gets undefined value when division by zero is performing, the rational function goes to $-\infty$ or to $+\infty$ as x approaches this value from positive or negative side, similar to the functions $\frac{1}{x}$ or $\frac{1}{x^2}$.

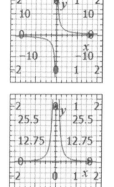

These are two standard simple cases (division by x *and by* x^2), is not allowed when x approaches 0 (*zero*); under this condition both graph approach y *axis* but never touch it. In this case, axis y is the vertical asymptote. If any $x - value$ makes the denominator equal to zero, in this position will be located the Vertical Asymptote.

Descriptive examples:

Function $f(x)$	$= \dfrac{5}{x-2}$	$= \dfrac{x}{x^2 - 4x - 12}$	$= \dfrac{2x^2}{x^2 + 4}$
Denominator analysis	$x - 2 = 0$ $x \neq 2$	$x^2 - 4x - 12 =$ $(x-6)(x+2)$ $= 0$ $x \neq 6 \; or \; x \neq -2$	$x^2 + 4 = 0$ produces imaginary solution $(x^2 + 4 \neq 0)$ $x = 2i$ $or \; x = -2i$
Domain	$(-\infty, 2)$ $\cup (2, \infty)$	$(-\infty, -2)$ $\cup (-2, 6) \cup (6, \infty)$	All Real numbers $\{R\}$
Vertical asymptote	$x = 2$	$x = 6 \; and \; x = -2$	None
Horizontal asymptote	$y_{h.a.} = 0$	$y_{h.a.} = 0$	$y_{h.a.} = 2$

The position of the	$$f(x) = \frac{ax^n + \cdots}{bx^m + \cdots}$$		
Horizontal Asymptote can be found follow the next rule:	If $n = m$	the Horizontal Asymptote is located at $y_{h.a.} = \dfrac{a}{b}$	
	If $n > m$	there is NO Horizontal Asymptote (will be slant asymptote)	
	If $n < m$	the Horizontal Asymptote is located at $y_{h.a.} = 0$	
Function $f(x)$	$= \dfrac{5}{x - 2}$	$= \dfrac{x}{x^2 - 4x - 12}$	$= \dfrac{2x^2}{x^2 + 4}$
$x - intercept$ exist when $y = 0$ (the numerator of the rational function is equal to 0).	No $x -$ intercept	$x - intercept.$ when $x = 0$	$x - intercept.$ when $x = 0$
$y - intercept$ exist only when $x = 0.$	$y = -\dfrac{5}{2}$	$y = 0$	$y = 0$
Graph			

When graphing rational function always follow the following points:

1. Domain,
2. Vertical, Horizontal and/or Slant Asymptotes,
3. X and Y Intercepts,
4. Increasing and Decreasing Intervals, and
5. Evaluating testing points.

EXAMPLE USING MICROSOFT MATHEMATICS ADD-IN

$$\text{GRAPH: } y = \frac{4x^2+1}{x^2-4x-12}$$

Determine the following characteristics:

Domain: (make the denominator equal to zero to analyze undefined situations) $x^2 - 4x - 12 = (x - 6)(x + 2) = 0$,

So, the Domain will be: $(\infty, -2) \cup (6. \infty)$; and correspondently,

In $x = -2$ and 6 are located the **Vertical Asymptotes**

The Horizontal Asymptote is located at: $\frac{4x^2}{1x^2} = 4$; at $y = 4$

$Y - intercept$, is located at $f(x = 0) = -1/12$

$X - intercepts$, are located at $f(x) = 0$,

$$4x^2 + 1 = 0$$

So $x = complex\ (imaginary)\ solution: There\ is\ not\ X_{intercept}$

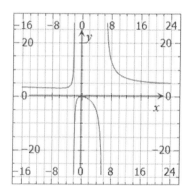

EXAMPLE USING WOLFRAM ALPHA MATHWORLD
LEARN ABOUT RATIONAL FUNCTIONS

Wolfram MathWorld™ the web's most extensive mathematics resource
Built with Mathematica Technology

https://mathworld.wolfram.com/RationalFunction.html

The following examples (screen shots) are interactive online exercises:

Simple Rational Functions

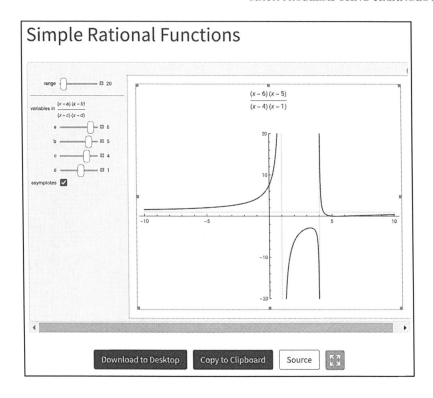

Analyze the Asymptotes:

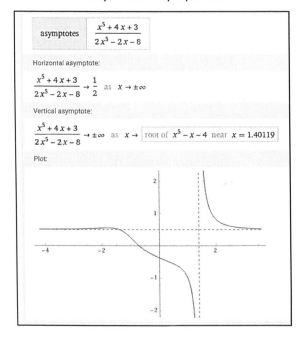

3.6. Polynomial and Rational Inequalities

Example 1:

Solve the following polynomial inequality

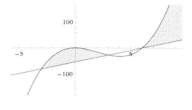

$x^3 - 6x^2 \geq 9x - 54$:

Using Wolfram Alpha, we can visualize the interceptions between two functions (upper figure):

$f_1(x) = x^3 - 6x^2$ and $f_2(x) = 9x - 54$

The interceptions between these two functions are the borders of the sectors were the statement expressed by the given inequality is true.

To provide effective solution we will apply more traditional method by creating a unique function: $f(x) = x^3 - 6x^2 - 9x + 54 \geq 0$

Factor by grouping and solve the equation:

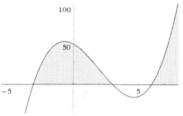

$$f(x) = x^3 - 6x^2 - 9x + 54 =$$
$$(x - 6)(x - 3)(x + 3) = 0$$
$$x = -3, \quad x = 3, \quad and \quad x = 6$$

Evidently, there are three points where the function $f(x)$ can change its sign from positive to negative and vice versa. In this case we have four intervals where the left part of the inequality may by greater or lesser than the right part of the given inequality. Also by testing these intervals, we can find the solution: $[-3, 3] \cup [6, \infty)$ as displayed in the graph.

Interval	$(-\infty, -3)$	$(-3. 3)$	$(3, 6)$	$(6, \quad \infty)$
Testing Points	$x = -5$	$x = 0$	$x = 4$	$x = 10$
Plugin the values (x)	$(-5)^3$ $- 6(-5)^2$ $\geq 9(-5)$ $- 54$	$(0)^3 - 6(0)^2$ $\geq 9(0) - 54$	$(4)^3$ $- 6(4)^2$ $\geq 9(4)$ $- 54$	$(10)^3 - 6(10)^2$ $\geq 9(10) - 54$
Statement	False	True: $[-3, 3]$	False	True: $[6, \infty)$

To graph the solution, we consider the segments were the inequality statement has true value. ($f(x) \geq 0$) in highlighted regions of the graph. Note that for set representation we have to use parenthesis if we do not touch the point (greater or less than) and bracket when touching the point (les tan or equal OR greater than or equal):

$[-3, 3] \cup [6, \infty)$

EXAMPLE USING WOLFRAM ALPHA ENGINE.

SOLVE THE FOLLOWING RATIONAL INEQUALITY $\dfrac{1}{x^2-4x-12} > \dfrac{1}{6-x}$

Firstly, create the function, arrange and make it equal to zero to analyze

$$f(x) = \frac{1}{(x^2-4x-12)} + \frac{1}{(x-6)} > 0.$$

Note that $(6 - x) = -(x - 6)$

STEP 1

Simplify the following:

$$\frac{1}{x^2 - 4x - 12} + \frac{1}{6-x}$$

STEP 2

> **Hint:** Put the fractions in $\dfrac{1}{x^2 - 4x - 12} + \dfrac{1}{6-x}$ over a common denominator.

Put each term in $\dfrac{1}{x^2 - 4x - 12} + \dfrac{1}{6-x}$ over the common denominator

$(x + 2)(6 - x)$: $\dfrac{1}{x^2 - 4x - 12} + \dfrac{1}{6-x} = \dfrac{\frac{(6-x)(x+2)}{x^2-4x-12}}{(6-x)(x+2)} + \dfrac{x+2}{(6-x)(x+2)}$:

$$\frac{\frac{(6-x)(x+2)}{x^2-4x-12}}{(6-x)(x+2)} + \frac{x+2}{(6-x)(x+2)}$$

STEP 3

> **Hint:** In $\dfrac{(6-x)(x+2)}{x^2-4x-12}$, $x+2$ in the numerator and the denominator have a non-trivial factor in common.

A common factor of $x + 2$ and $x^2 - 4x - 12$ is $x + 2$, so $\dfrac{(6-x)(x+2)}{x^2-4x-12} =$

$\dfrac{(6-x)(x+2)}{(x-6)(x+2)}$:

$$\frac{\frac{(6-x)(x+2)}{(x-6)(x+2)}}{(6-x)(x+2)} + \frac{x+2}{(6-x)(x+2)}$$

STEP 4

Hint: Cancel terms in $\dfrac{(6-x)(x+2)}{(x-6)(x+2)}$.

Cancel terms. $\dfrac{(6-x)(x+2)}{(x-6)(x+2)} = \dfrac{6-x}{x-6}$:

$$\dfrac{\frac{6-x}{x-6}}{(6-x)(x+2)} + \dfrac{x+2}{(6-x)(x+2)}$$

STEP 5

Hint: In $\dfrac{6-x}{x-6}$, the numerator and the denominator have a non-trivial factor in common.

Factor -1 from $6-x$:

$$\dfrac{\frac{-(x-6)}{x-6}}{(6-x)(x+2)} + \dfrac{x+2}{(6-x)(x+2)}$$

STEP 6

Hint: Combine products of like terms.

$\dfrac{-(x-6)}{x-6} = -(x-6)^{1-1}$:

$$\dfrac{-(x-6)^{1-1}}{(6-x)(x+2)} + \dfrac{x+2}{(6-x)(x+2)}$$

STEP 7

Hint: Look for the difference of two identical terms.

$1 - 1 = 0$:

$$\dfrac{x+2}{(6-x)(x+2)} - \dfrac{(x-6)^{0}}{(6-x)(x+2)}$$

STEP 8

Hint: Combine $\dfrac{x+2}{(6-x)(x+2)} - \dfrac{(x-6)^{0}}{(6-x)(x+2)}$ into a single fraction.

$$\dfrac{x+2}{(6-x)(x+2)} - \dfrac{(x-6)^{0}}{(6-x)(x+2)} = \dfrac{(x+2)-1}{(6-x)(x+2)}$$

$$\dfrac{x-1+2}{(6-x)(x+2)}$$

STEP 9

Hint: Add the numbers in $x - 1 + 2$ together.

Add like terms. $2 - 1 = 1$:

Answer:

$$\dfrac{x+1}{(6-x)(x+2)}$$

Now, solve

$$-\dfrac{x+1}{(x-6)(x+2)} > 0$$

We can continue with Wolfram Alpha (step-by-step) or check with another graphic utility to see the solution set $(-\infty, -2) \cup (0.083, 6)$

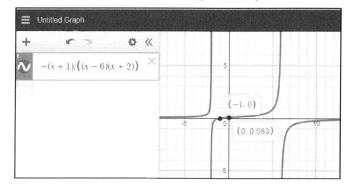

EXAMPLE USING TI GRAPHIC CALCULATOR.
LEARN HOW TO SOLVE POLYNOMIAL INEQUALITIES

You also can use previously implemented technological utilities.

Model-I

To solve a polynomial inequality, we have to understand the statement given by the inequality. Always it is referred to the x values that make the inequality a true statement. For example, let's suppose that we want to solve the following inequality:

$$x^3 - 6x^2 \geq 9x - 54$$

The statement says that there is (are) one (some) x value(s) for which the function $f_1(x) = x^3 - 6x^2$ is greater than the function $f_2(x) = 9x - 54$

The traditional method for solving inequalities is based on the creation of unique polynomial function as follow:

$$f(x) = x^3 - 6x^2 - 9x + 54 \geq 0$$

In this case the first step in solving a polynomial inequality is to find the polynomial's zeroes (its x-intercepts).

Between any two consecutive zeroes, the polynomial will be either positive or negative. Since the inequality is asking for positivity ("greater than zero") or negativity ("less than zero"), finding the intercepts ("equal to zero") is the way to get started. We can think about the problem graphically, the zeroes are the points where the polynomial crosses or touch the x-axis; between any two consecutive crossing-points, the polynomial will either be above the axis (and thus positive) or below it (and thus negative).

To find the zeros in the previously given example, we can factor by grouping and solve the equation. Making it equal to zero to apply the zero product rule we get:

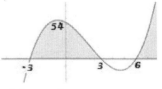

$$f(x) = x^3 - 6x^2 - 9x + 54 = (x - 6)(x - 3)(x + 3) = 0$$
$$x = -3, \quad x = 3, \quad and \quad x = 6$$

These three zeroes divide the x-axis into four intervals:

(–infinity, –3), (–3, 3), (3, 6), and (6, +infinity).

We need to figure out on which of these intervals the polynomial's graph is above the x-axis. As we know this is a third degree polynomial, opens up on the right side, x-intercepts located at $x = -3$, $x = 3$, and $x = 6$ and y-intercept at $y = 54$. The solution set will be (in set notation) or graphically: $[-3, 3] \cup [6, \infty)$.

Model-II

As you can see, being familiar with polynomials and their shapes facilitates getting the solution. But what if you haven't learned about their shapes, or if the polynomial is more complicated, or if you have to "show your reasoning"?

Let's re-work the above exercise using the "factor method".

Factor the polynomial and find the solution: $(x - 6)(x - 3)(x + 3) \geq 0$

The factors give the zeroes of the polynomial, and the zeroes give the following intervals of positivity and negativity: (–infinity, –3), (–3, 3), (3, 6), and (6, +infinity).

We just need to figure out which intervals are positive and which are negative. I've got three factors, so I'll draw up a table of factors with the intervals (Sectors marked off):

Evidently, there are three points where the function $f(x)$ can change its sign from positive to negative and vice versa. In this case we have four intervals (Sectors) where the left part of the inequality may by greater or lesser than the right part of the given inequality. Also by testing these intervals, we can find the solution: $[-3, 3] \cup [6, \infty)$ as displayed in the graph.

For testing purposes we use any number from the interval Sectors I, II, II, and IV); for example, x=-5 in Sector-I, x=0 in Sector-II, x=4 in Sector-III, and x=10 in Sector-IV

Sector	I	II	III	IV
Testing Points	$x = -5$	$x = 0$	$x = 4$	$x = 10$
Plugin x values	$(-5)^3 - 6(-5)^2$ $\geq 9(-5) - 54$	$(0)^3 - 6(0)^2$ $\geq 9(0) - 54$	$(4)^3 - 6(4)^2$ $\geq 9(4) - 54$	$(10)^3 - 6(10)^2$ $\geq 9(10) - 54$
Statement	False	True: $[-3, 3]$	False	True: $[6, \infty)$

Now we can read the solution off the table. We need the intervals where the polynomial is positive (True), so I'll pick the intervals that have a positive value. With another words;

To graph the solution, we consider the intervals were the inequality statement has true value. $(f(x) \geq 0)$ in highlighted regions. Note that for set representation we have to use parenthesis if we do not touch the point (greater or less than) and bracket when touching the point (les tan or equal OR greater than or equal):

Similar to the previous solution method (**Model-I**), the solution set and it graphic representation will be: $[-3, 3] \cup [6, \infty)$.

On the infinite side goes parenthesis because we never touch the infinite.

Model-III. Application of Graphing Calculator using two function:

$$x^3 - 6x^2 \geq 9x - 54$$

The statement says that there is (are) one or some values of x for which the function $f_1(x) = x^3 - 6x^2$ is greater than the function $f_2(x) = 9x - 54$

Using a graphic calculator, we can visualize the graph of the two given functions: $f_1(x) = x^3 - 6x^2$ and $f_2(x) = 9x - 54$

The interceptions between these two functions are the borders of the sectors were the statement expressed by the given inequality is true; where

$$f_1(x) \geq f_2(x)$$

Equations	Graph of $f_1(x) \ and \ f_2(x)$	Convenient Window
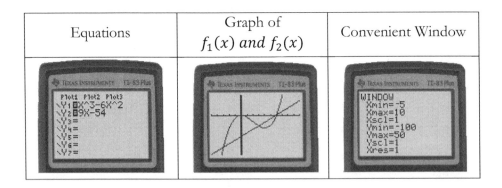		

To select the Sectors (intervals or partitions of the Domain) where the inequality statement is a true or false statement, we have to determine in which *x − values $f_1(x)$ is greater or equal to $f_2(x)$.* Graphing both functions we get:

Both Graph together and analysis of the Interceptions		
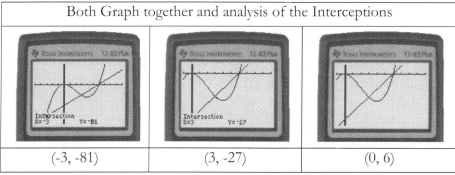		
(-3, -81)	(3, -27)	(0, 6)

We can visualize that in the *x − intervals* $[−3, 3]$ *and* $[6, ∞]$ the function $f_1(x)$ goes over the function $f_2(x)$, means that first function is greater than the second. They can be equals at the interception point, because the statement a priory stablishes that the first function is greater or equal to the second one ($≤$ *or* $≥$). To represent this condition, we use brake instead parenthesis. Parenthesis have to be used when using the symbols greater than or less than ($<$ *or* $>$), excluding the equality component. We can repeat previous representation of the solution:

Or in set notation: $[−3, 3]$ U $[6, ∞)$.

Model-IV. Graphic Calculator using unique polynomial function.

$$f(x) = x^3 − 6x^2 − 9x + 54 ≥ 0$$

Second graphic option	Function	Convenient Window
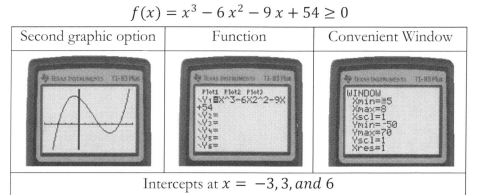		
Intercepts at $x = −3, 3,$ *and* 6		

Obviously, the solution can be written similar to the previously provided answer: $[−3, 3]$ U $[6, ∞)$.

CHAPTER-4
Exponential and Logarithmic Functions

In Chapter V not all solutions to the homework exercises are provided in this notebook; at this level students have to be able to manage Mathematics and Wolfram-Alpha programs to complete their homework. If you have trouble solving any exercise, bring your question to the class.

4.1. Inverse Functions

In Algebra, every operation is paired with its "opposite" (inverse): Addition with Subtraction, Multiplication with Division, Powers with Roots, and Reciprocals with Reciprocals. In functional terms, inverse function is the function obtained by expressing the dependent variable of one function as the independent variable of another; in other words; we interchange x withy to find the inverse function.

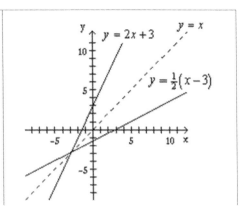

We have Inverted our functions

If f expresses a functional relationship between x and y, so that $y = f(x)$, and if f is invertible, then f^{-1} expresses the reverse relationship, $x = f^{-1}(y)$.

EXAMPLE USING MICROSOFT MATHEMATICS ADD-IN:

Linear Function $y = 2x + 3$

Inverse substitution: $x = 2y + 3$

Solving for y: $x = 2y + 3$

$$y = \tfrac{1}{2}(x - 3)$$

The graphs of a function and its inverse function are symmetric with respect to the line $y = x$

Quadratic Function $y = x^2 - 2$

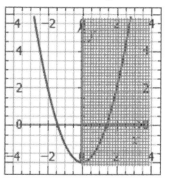

Inverse substitution: $x = y^2 - 2$

Solving for y: $y = \sqrt{x + 2}$, valid only for $x \geq 0$

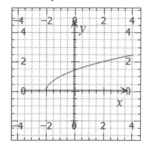

Fact: The composition of any function and it inverse, is a new function (represented by y) equal to x

$$(f \mathbf{o} f^{-1})(x) = f(f^{-1}(x)) \quad \text{or} \quad (f^{-1} \mathbf{o} f)(x) = f^{-1}(f(x))$$

Example: Given $f = 2x + 3$ and $f^{-1} = \frac{1}{2}(x - 3)$; the composition will be:

$$f(f^{-1}(x)) = 2\left[\frac{1}{2}(x - 3)\right] + 3 = x - 3 + 3 = x$$

4.2. Exponential Functions

An exponential function is a mathematical expression in which a variable represents the exponent of an expression.

For example: $y = 2^x$,This simplest equation, it is read as "y equals 2 to the x power;" the graph is displayed on the right.

$$y = 2^x$$

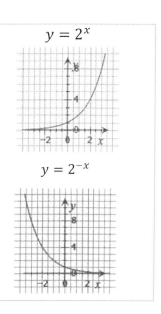

If $y = 2^{-x}$, we can plot the graph point by point, providing **x-values** and calculating its corresponding y; or, we can apply transformation, by reflecting the graph towards axis y (on the right)

$$y = 2^{-x}$$

General Properties:

$y = a^x$, where a - is the basis, x the variable, and y the function

Note than a can not be a negative number and exist in the following intervals: $(0, 1) \cup (1, \infty)$

1. Lets suppose that a is a negative number. When the exponent x is even the function has positive value, when the exponent is odd number, the function will be negative. So, the function will not be exponential, it will be a periodic function changing its value from negative to positive and vice verse

2. If $a = 0$, there is not function.

3. If $a = 1$, also there is not a function as one (1) to any power is equal to one (1).

4. When $0 < a < 1$ the function opens up on the left side:

$$y = 2^{-x} = \frac{1}{2^x} = \frac{1^x}{2^x} = \left(\frac{1}{2}\right)^x = (0.5)^x$$

5. When $a > 1$ the function opens up on the right side.

6. The DOMAIN of the exponential function is: Any real number $(-\infty, \infty)$ and the RANGE $(0. \infty)$

EXAMPLE USING MICROSOFT MATHEMATICS.
GRAPHING EXPONENTIAL FUNCTIONS

Graphing exponential functions $y = 2^{x+2} - 3$ using transformation:

$y = 2^x$	$y = 2^{x+2}$	$y = 2^{x+2} - 3$
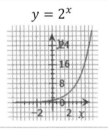	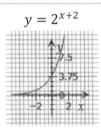	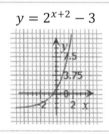

Graphing exponential functions $y = -2^{x+2} + 5$ using transformation:

$y = 2^x$	$y = 2^{x+2}$	$y = -2^{x+2}$	$y = -2^{x+2} + 5$
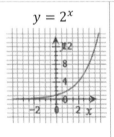	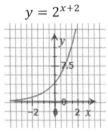	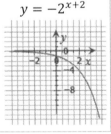	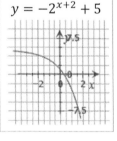

4.3. Logarithmic Functions

Giving exponential function $y = a^x$; its inverse will be: $x = a^y$

To solve for y we can use graphic method (on the right).

Using traditional procedures we can not solve the inverse exponential function. However, a new method was adopted by representing the solution as follow:

$$y = \log_a x$$

If x and a are real positive numbers such that $a \neq 1$, then

$y = \log_a x$ is called the logarithmic function with base a of x.

$$y = \log_a x \quad \text{and} \quad x = a^y$$

are equivalent.

DOMAIN of the logarithmic function is $(0. \infty)$, RANGE $(-\infty, \infty)$

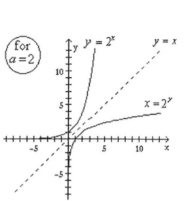

(for $a=2$)

The logarithmic function is the reflection of the exponential function towards the axis $y = x$

Logarithmic function is a representation of the solution of the inverse exponential function as we can see on the next examples/illustrations:

$y = \log_2 x$	$x = 2^y$	$y = \log_{10} 10 = 1$	$10 = 10^1$
$y = \log_4 x$	$x = 4^y$	$y = \log_{10} 100 = 2$	$100 = 10^2$
$y - 1 = \log_3 x$	$x = 3^{(y-1)}$	$y = \log_5 25 = 2$	$25 = 5^2$
$2 = \log_8 \frac{1}{3}$	$2 = \sqrt[3]{8}$	$\log_{25} 5 = \frac{1}{2}$	$5 = \sqrt{25}$ $= (25)^{\frac{1}{2}}$

Further representation: $\log_{10}(...) = \log(...)$ and $\log_e(...) = \ln(...)$, named natural logarithm (Definition of e=2.71828 further will be discussed).

EXAMPLE USING MICROSOFT MATHEMATICS
GRAPHING LOGARITHMIC FUNCTIONS

Graphing exponential functions $y = \log(x - 3) + 5$ using transformation:

$y = \log(x)$	$y = \log(x - 3)$	$y = \log(x - 3) + 5$
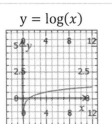		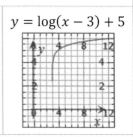

Graphing exponential functions $y = -\log(x - 3) + 5$ using transformation:

$y = \log(x)$	$y = \log(x - 3)$	$y = -\log(x - 3)$	$y = -\log(x - 3) + 5$
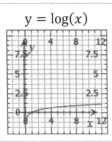	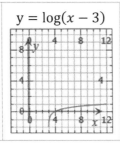	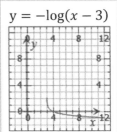	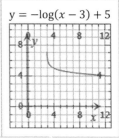

Properties of Logarithms

1	$\log_a a = 1$ because $a = a^1$
2	$\log_a 1 = 0$ because $1 = a^0$
3	$\log_a a^x = x$ because $a^x = a^x$
4	$a^{\log_a x} = x$ because $\log_a x = \log_a x$
5	$\log_b(xy) = \log_b x + \log_b y.$
6	$\log_b(x/y) = \log_b x - \log_b y.$
7	$\log_b(x^n) = n \log_b x.$
8	$\log_b x = \log_a x / \log_a b$

Example 1: Condense.

$\frac{1}{2}\log_2(x)^4 + 4\log_2\left(\sqrt{x-2}\right) - \log_2(x-2) =$ $= \log_2\left(\sqrt{(x)^4}\right) + \log_2\left(\sqrt{(x-2)^4}\right) - \log_2(x-2) =$ $\log_2[(x)^2\frac{(x-2)^2}{(x-2)}] = \log_2[x^2\,(x-2)]$	Property # 3, them properties 5 and 6, and simplify.

Example2: Expand.

$\log\dfrac{x^3(y-2)}{\sqrt{(x+2)^5}} =$ $= \log[x^3(y-2) - \log\sqrt{(x+2)^5} = \log(x^3) +$ $\log(y-2) - \frac{5}{2}\log(x+2) =$ $= 3\log(x) + \log(y-2) - \frac{5}{2}\log(x+2)$	Poperty # 6, them properties 5 and 7

Example 3: Apply property 4

$5^{\log_5 16} = 16$ Consider this expression in exponential format. We can demonstrate that it is true rewriting in logarithmic format $\log_5 16 = \log_5 16$	Because $a = 5$ is the bases, $y = \log_5 16$ is the function, and $x = 16$ is the argument.

Example 4: Apply Formula Base Change.

Previous example: $5^{\log_5 16} = 16$

$log(5^{\log_5 16}) = log16;$ so: $[\log_5 16][log5] = log16$

Resulting: $[\log_5 16] = \dfrac{log16}{log5}$

Numeric and graphic solution: $[\log_5 16] = \dfrac{\log 16}{\log 5} = \dfrac{1.20411}{0.60943} =$ $=1.72271...$	$y = \dfrac{\log(x)}{\log(5)}$

4.4. Exponential and Logarithmic Equations

Introductory Exponential Equation Examples (notably more difficult examples will be solved during the lecture):

Example 1.

Same Base

$$5^x = 5^{2x-3}$$

$$x = 2x - 3$$

$$3 = x$$

Example 2.

Creating same Base

$$3^{2x-3} = 27$$

$$3^{2x-3} = 3^3,$$

So: $2x - 3 = 3$,

$$2x = 6,$$

$$x = 3$$

Example 3.

Creating same Base

$$4^{x^2} = \left(\frac{1}{16}\right)^{-3x+4}$$

$$4^{x^2} = \left(\frac{1}{4^2}\right)^{-3x+4}$$

$$4^{x^2} = (4^{-2})^{-3x+4}$$

$$4^{x^2} = (4)^{6x-8}$$

$$x^2 = 6x - 8$$

$$x^2 - 6x + 8 = 0$$

$$(x-4)(x-2) = 0$$

$$x = 4, \quad x = 2$$

Example 4.

Using log when there is not whole exponent using same base:

$$3^x = 8$$

In this example

$(3^{What\ number} = 8)$

So, we apply logarithms:

$$\log 3^x = \log 8$$

$$x \log 3 = \log 8$$

$$x = \frac{\log 8}{\log 3}$$

$$= \frac{0.903089987...}{0.477121255...}$$

$$x = 1.892789261...$$

In this example we can use log or ln.

No whole exponent was found:

$$3^{1.892789261} = 8$$

Next examples are useful to get general idea:

Introductory Logarithmic Equation Examples:

Example 1.

Equal arguments

$$\log_a(x-2) = \log_a(3x-8)$$
$$x - 2 = 3x - 8$$
$$6 = 2x, \text{ so, } x = 3$$

This example can be solved using quotient rule and logarithmic definition (see on the right)

$$\log_a(x-2) - \log_a(3x-8) = 0$$
$$\log_a \frac{x-2}{3x-8} = 0$$
$$\frac{x-2}{3x-8} = a^0 = 1$$
$$x - 2 = 3x - 8 \ldots so \ \ x = 3$$

Example 2.

Applying properties of logarithm:
$$\log_2(x-2) + \log_2(x) = 3$$

Apply product rule
$$\log_2[x(x-2)] = 3$$
Apply definition property:
$$[x(x-2)] = 2^3 = 8$$
$$x^2 - 2x - 8 = 0$$
$$(x-4)(x+2) = 0$$
$$x = 4 \ and \ x = -2$$
Reject $x = -2$

Example 3.

Applying properties of logarithm:
$$\log_3(x+5) - \log_3(x-3) = 2$$

Apply quotient rule
$$\log_3 \left[\frac{x+5}{x-3}\right] = 2$$
Apply definition property:
$$\frac{x+5}{x-3} = 3^2 = 9$$
$$(x-5) = 9(x-3)$$
$$x + 5 = 9x - 27$$
$$32 = 8x, \ so \ \ x = 4$$

4.5. Compound Interest.

4.2.1. Yearly simple interest:

$$A = P(1 + r)$$

Where: $P =$ Principal, $A(t) =$ the Actual Amount at simple yearly interest rate r

Example 1:

Suppose you want to open an account with $5,000 in a bank (on January 1st), which pays 3.5% yearly. Determine how much money you will have at the end of the year.

$$A = 5000 \, (1.035) = \$5175.00$$

4.2.2.   Periodically Compounded:

Year	Actual money at the end of the year.	
1	$A = P + Pr = P(1 + r)$	
2	$\begin{aligned} A &= P(1+r) + P(1+r)r \\ &= P(1+r)(1+r) \\ &= P(1+r)^2 \end{aligned}$	The money at the beginning of each year is de accumulated amount at the end of the pre- vious year
3	$\begin{aligned} A &= P(1+r)^2 + P(1+r)^2 r \\ &= P(1+r)^2(1+r) \\ &= P(1+r)^3 \end{aligned}$	
t	$A = P(1+r)^t$	

Example 2:

Suppose you want to open an account with $5,000 in a bank (on January 1st), which pays 3.5% yearly. Determine how much money you will have in 5 full years.

$$A = 5000(1 + 0.035)^5 = \$5938.43$$

If calculating monthly instead yearly we have to use 12 period per year (per month), also we have to consider monthly interest rate. If consider daily, we have to use 365 periods per years and reduce yearly interest rate to daily rate, etc.

In general form we can write a periodically compounded interest formula as follow: $A = P\left(1 + \dfrac{r}{n}\right)^{nt}$

Where: $t =$ Total time in years, $n =$ Number of compounding periods per year (note that the total number of compounding periods is $n \times t$)

98

and $r =$ Nominal annual interest rate expressed as a decimal. e.g.: 6% = 0.06

Example 3:

Suppose you want to open a secure saving account compounded quarterly with a $5,000.00 in a bank (on January 1st), which pays 1.2% yearly. Determine how much money you will have in 5 years. (in this case n=4)

$$A = 5000\left(1 + \frac{0.012}{4}\right)^{(4)(5)} = \$5308.71$$

4.2.3.   Continuously Compounded:

As n, the number of compounding periods per year, increases without limit, we get a new equation:

$$A = P\left(1 + \frac{r}{n}\right)^{nt} = P\left[\left(1 + \frac{1}{h}\right)^{h}\right]^{rt} = Pe^{rt}$$

Where we have replaced $\frac{n}{r} = h,\ so\ \frac{1}{h} = \frac{r}{n}, and\ n = hr.$ See example 264 on page 117 for $\left(1 + \frac{1}{h}\right)^{h} = e$

Example 4:

Suppose you want to open an account with $5,000 in a bank (on January 1st), which pays 3.5% continuously compounded. Determine how much money you will have in 5 full years.

$$Pe^{rt} = 5000e^{(0.035)(5)} = \$5956.23$$

4.6.   Exponential Growth and Decay:

The exponential growth at time can be written as:

$$N = N_0 e^{rt}$$

Where: N_0 - is the starting population, N - is the population after a certain time, t , has elapsed, and e - is the

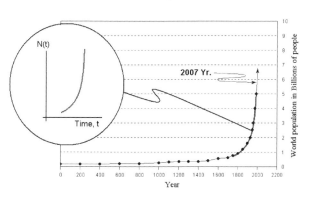

99

base of natural logarithms (Nipper constant = 2.71828...). r is the rate of increase (rate of growth), always positive.

On the right, plotted dots are values known from census and historical estimates of world population, while the continuous line is the graphic solution of the previous equation.

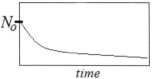

time

The exponential Decay or simple Decay (graphically represented also on the right) is the same exponential process but the constant < 0, so the amount decreases in time.

EXAMPLE USING WOLFRAM ALPHA.
LEARN EXPONENTIAL AND LOGARITHMIC FUNCTIONS

Solve any type of exponential and/or logarithmic transformation, equations, and its graph.

https://mathworld.wolfram.com/ExponentialFunction.html

https://mathworld.wolfram.com/Logarithm.html

EXAMPLE USING WOLFRAM ALPHA.
LEARN ABOUT COMPOUND INTEREST AND CONTINUOUSLY COMPOUNDED

Input:

$$x = 1000\left(1 + \frac{0.08}{1}\right)^{5\times 1}$$

Result:

$$x = 1469.33$$

Number line:

https://www.wolframalpha.com/widgets/view.jsp?id=b8043a6eb1c32bb77caff313af9d069d

Wolfram|Alpha Widgets

Overview   Tour   Gallery

Interest Compounding Continuously

BETA

e^(.04

x   15

Submit

WolframAlpha

https://www.wolframalpha.com/widgets/view.jsp?id=29a77d08005e3e589b7e01e8a915cb74

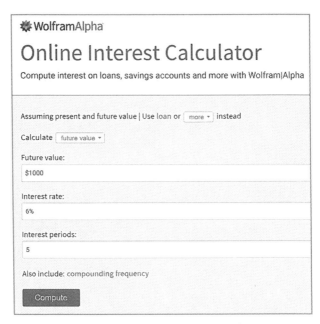

https://www.wolframalpha.com/calculators/interest-calculator

EXAMPLE USING WOLFRAM ALPHA.
LEARN ABOUT GROWTH AND DECAY

https://www.wolframalpha.com/widg-
ets/view.jsp?id=eac0e1668bd47e486ee907ab14ddbedd

CHAPTER-5. System of Equations

5.1. System of Linear Equations in Two and Three Variables

System of linear equations in two variables (x, y) are represented by two line

$$y_1 = m_1 x_1 + b_1$$
$$y_2 = m_2 x_2 + b_2$$

The solution of the system exist when the ordinates get the same value $y_1 = y_2 = y_o$ at the matching abscise $x_1 = x_2 = x_0$. In that case, both lines intercept at this specific point (x_0, y_0).

Example; given the following two equations (to lines on the right) their interception represents the solution of the system:

$$y = 4x + 10$$
$$y = -2x + 22$$

The solution (interception) exist at:

$$(x = 2 \ and \ y = 18)$$

Graph using Microsoft Mathematics Add-in, in Word Document.

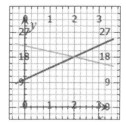

System of linear equations in three variables (x,y,z) represent three planes (surfaces). Similar to 2 by 2 systems, in 3 by 3 systems the solution exist at the interception point.

$$a_1 x - b_1 y + c_1 z = d_1$$
$$a_2 x - b_2 y + c_2 z = d_2$$
$$a_3 x - b_3 y + c_3 z = d_3$$

System of linear equations can be solved using different methods: addition/subtraction (also called elimination method), substitution method, matrix and/or matrix based method (also called Kramer's' Rule).

For linear system in three variables the most common method is addition/subtraction. To solve a system, we have to follow the following steps:

1. Pick any two pairs of equations from the system.
2. Eliminate the same variable from each pair.
3. Solve the system of the two new equations
4. Substitute the solution back into one of the original equations and solve for the third variable.
5. Check by plugging the solution into one of the other three equations.

EXAMPLE USING MICROSOFT MATHEMATICS ADD-IN
SOLVE THE SYSTEM OF LINEAR EQUATIONS

$:4x - 3y + z = -10$ $2x + y + 3z = 0$ $-x + 2y - 5z = 17$	1. Use Microsoft Mathematics to graph and to solve. Step-by-step solution by eliminating one of the variables (Elimination Method)
$4x - 3y + z = -10$ $2x + y + 3z = 0$	2. Pick any two equations:
$4x - 3y + z = -10$ $6x + 3y + 9z = 0$	3. Eliminate one of the variable by multiplying the second equation by 3, them **add both equations.**
$\mathbf{10x + 10z = -10}$	4. Add both equations: resulting in a new *2 by 2* equation
$2x + y + 3z = 0$ $-x + 2y - 5z = 17$	5. Pick any other two equations.
$-4x - 2y - 6z = 0$ $-x + 2y - 5z = 17$	6. Eliminate the same variable multiplying the first equation by negative two (-2)
$-5x - 11z = 17$	7. Add both equations: resulting in a new 2 by 2 equation
$10x + 10z = -10$ $-5x - 11z = 17$	8. Use the equations obtained in points (3) and (6), and solve the *2 by 2* system
$10x + 10z = -10$ $-10x - 22z = 34$	9. Multiply the second equation by 2 and add both equations to eliminate x variable
$12z = 24$ or $z = -2$	10. Resulting in $z = -2$
$10x + 10(-2) = -10$	11. Replace z value in any of the equation obtained in (3) or (6), and get *x value* $(x = 1)$
Finally the solution (interception point between the three planes) is: $(x = 1, y = 4, z = -2)$	12. Replace *x and z values* in any one of the original equations and get *y value* 13. So you have $x, y, and\ z\ values$.

Using different software, your ca reach the same results.

When eliminating one of the variables you can sue different couple of equation as can be seen in the next technology example.

On the right graphic representation of the system generated by Microsoft Mathematics Add-in.

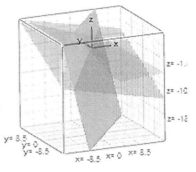

EXAMPLE USING WOLFRAM ALPHA ENGINE.
SOLVE THE SYSTEM OF LINEAR EQUATIONS APPLYING ELIMINATION METHOD.

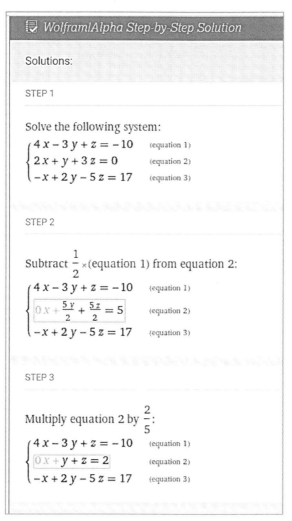

☑ *WolframlAlpha Step-by-Step Solution*

Solutions:

STEP 1

Solve the following system:
$$\begin{cases} 4x - 3y + z = -10 & \text{(equation 1)} \\ 2x + y + 3z = 0 & \text{(equation 2)} \\ -x + 2y - 5z = 17 & \text{(equation 3)} \end{cases}$$

STEP 2

Subtract $\dfrac{1}{2} \times$(equation 1) from equation 2:
$$\begin{cases} 4x - 3y + z = -10 & \text{(equation 1)} \\ 0x + \dfrac{5y}{2} + \dfrac{5z}{2} = 5 & \text{(equation 2)} \\ -x + 2y - 5z = 17 & \text{(equation 3)} \end{cases}$$

STEP 3

Multiply equation 2 by $\dfrac{2}{5}$:
$$\begin{cases} 4x - 3y + z = -10 & \text{(equation 1)} \\ 0x + y + z = 2 & \text{(equation 2)} \\ -x + 2y - 5z = 17 & \text{(equation 3)} \end{cases}$$

STEP 4

Add $\frac{1}{4}\times$(equation 1) to equation 3:

$$\begin{cases} 4x - 3y + z = -10 & \text{(equation 1)} \\ 0x + y + z = 2 & \text{(equation 2)} \\ \boxed{0x + \frac{5y}{4} - \frac{19z}{4} = \frac{29}{2}} & \text{(equation 3)} \end{cases}$$

STEP 5

Multiply equation 3 by 4:

$$\begin{cases} 4x - 3y + z = -10 & \text{(equation 1)} \\ 0x + y + z = 2 & \text{(equation 2)} \\ \boxed{0x + 5y - 19z = 58} & \text{(equation 3)} \end{cases}$$

STEP 6

Swap equation 2 with equation 3:

$$\begin{cases} 4x - 3y + z = -10 & \text{(equation 1)} \\ \boxed{0x + 5y - 19z = 58} & \text{(equation 2)} \\ \boxed{0x + y + z = 2} & \text{(equation 3)} \end{cases}$$

STEP 7

Subtract $\frac{1}{5}\times$(equation 2) from equation 3:

$$\begin{cases} 4x - 3y + z = -10 & \text{(equation 1)} \\ 0x + 5y - 19z = 58 & \text{(equation 2)} \\ \boxed{0x + 0y + \frac{24z}{5} = -\frac{48}{5}} & \text{(equation 3)} \end{cases}$$

STEP 8

Multiply equation 3 by $\frac{5}{24}$:

$$\begin{cases} 4x - 3y + z = -10 & \text{(equation 1)} \\ 0x + 5y - 19z = 58 & \text{(equation 2)} \\ \boxed{0x + 0y + z = -2} & \text{(equation 3)} \end{cases}$$

STEP 9

Add $19 \times$(equation 3) to equation 2:
$$\begin{cases} 4x - 3y + z = -10 & \text{(equation 1)} \\ 0x + 5y + 0z = 20 & \text{(equation 2)} \\ 0x + 0y + z = -2 & \text{(equation 3)} \end{cases}$$

STEP 10

Divide equation 2 by 5:
$$\begin{cases} 4x - 3y + z = -10 & \text{(equation 1)} \\ 0x + y + 0z = 4 & \text{(equation 2)} \\ 0x + 0y + z = -2 & \text{(equation 3)} \end{cases}$$

STEP 11

Add $3 \times$(equation 2) to equation 1:
$$\begin{cases} 4x + 0y + z = 2 & \text{(equation 1)} \\ 0x + y + 0z = 4 & \text{(equation 2)} \\ 0x + 0y + z = -2 & \text{(equation 3)} \end{cases}$$

STEP 12

Subtract equation 3 from equation 1:
$$\begin{cases} 4x + 0y + 0z = 4 & \text{(equation 1)} \\ 0x + y + 0z = 4 & \text{(equation 2)} \\ 0x + 0y + z = -2 & \text{(equation 3)} \end{cases}$$

STEP 13

Divide equation 1 by 4:
$$\begin{cases} x + 0y + 0z = 1 & \text{(equation 1)} \\ 0x + y + 0z = 4 & \text{(equation 2)} \\ 0x + 0y + z = -2 & \text{(equation 3)} \end{cases}$$

Resulting $x = 1, y = 4, z = -2$

5.2. Systems of Linear Equations and Matrixes.

In this section, we will study the Matrix method for solving systems of equations. The Matrix method named Gauss-Jordan Elimination Method operates on the basis of Augmented Matrices.

An **augmented matrix** for a system of equations is a matrix of numbers in which each row represents the constants from each equations. For the following system:

$$a_1x + b_1y + c_1z = d_1$$
$$a_2x + b_2y + c_2z = d_2$$
$$a_3x + b_3y + c_3z = d_3$$

The augmented matrix has to be written as:

$$\begin{vmatrix} a_1 & b_1 & c_1 & d_1 \\ a_2 & b_2 & c_2 & d_2 \\ a_3 & b_3 & c_3 & d_3 \end{vmatrix}$$

If we could rewrite previous matrix in the form of identity matrix (all elements are 0 except the diagonals, equal to 1):

$$\begin{vmatrix} 1 & 0 & 0 & l \\ 0 & 1 & 0 & m \\ 0 & 0 & 1 & n \end{vmatrix}$$

It would represent the solution of the system of linear equations, where

$$x = l, \quad y = m, \quad and \quad z = n$$

Example 1:

$$x - 2y + 3z = 7$$
$$2x + y + z = 4$$
$$-3x + 2y - 2z = -10$$

The augmented matrix:

$$\begin{vmatrix} 1 & -2 & 3 & 7 \\ 2 & 1 & 1 & 4 \\ -3 & 2 & -2 & -10 \end{vmatrix}$$

Which we will represent in form of table to facilitate further description of the solution process:

1	-2	3	7
2	1	1	4
-3	2	-2	-10

Elementary row operations to produce the identity Matrix:

1. $R_2 = (R_2 - 2R_1)$	2. $R_3 = (R_3 + 3R_1)$	3. $R_2 = (R_2/5)$
<table><tr><td>1</td><td>-2</td><td>3</td><td>7</td></tr><tr><td>0</td><td>5</td><td>-5</td><td>-10</td></tr><tr><td>-3</td><td>2</td><td>-2</td><td>-10</td></tr></table>	<table><tr><td>1</td><td>-2</td><td>3</td><td>7</td></tr><tr><td>0</td><td>5</td><td>-5</td><td>-10</td></tr><tr><td>-3</td><td>2</td><td>-2</td><td>-10</td></tr></table>	<table><tr><td>1</td><td>-2</td><td>3</td><td>7</td></tr><tr><td>0</td><td>1</td><td>-1</td><td>-2</td></tr><tr><td>0</td><td>-4</td><td>7</td><td>11</td></tr></table>

4. $R_3 = (4R_2 + R_3)$	5. $R_3 = (R_3/3)$	6. $(R_1 + R_2)$

1	-2	3	7
0	1	-1	-2
0	**0**	**3**	**3**

1	-2	3	7
0	1	-1	-2
0	**0**	**1**	**1**

1	-2	3	7
0	**1**	**0**	**-1**
0	0	1	1

7. $R_1 = (R_1 - 3R_3)$	8. $R_1 = (2R_2 + R_1)$	

1	**-2**	**0**	**4**
0	1	0	-1
0	0	1	1

1	**0**	**0**	**2**
0	1	0	-1
0	0	1	1

The resulting solution set will be:

$$x = 2, \quad y = -1, \quad z = 1$$

EXAMPLE USING WOLFRAM ALPHA ENGINE.
USE GAUSSIAN ELIMINATION MATRIX METHOD.

$$2x - y + z = 7$$
$$4x - 2y - z = -1$$
$$x + 3y + 2z = 25$$

2x-y+z=7, 4x-2y-z=-1, x+3y+2z=25

> **WolframlAlpha Step-by-Step Solution**
>
> Solutions:
>
> STEP 1
>
> Solve the following system:
> $$\begin{cases} 2x - y + z = 7 \\ 4x - 2y - z = -1 \\ x + 3y + 2z = 25 \end{cases}$$
>
> STEP 2
>
> Express the system in matrix form:
> $$\begin{pmatrix} 2 & -1 & 1 \\ 4 & -2 & -1 \\ 1 & 3 & 2 \end{pmatrix} \begin{pmatrix} x \\ y \\ z \end{pmatrix} = \begin{pmatrix} 7 \\ -1 \\ 25 \end{pmatrix}$$

STEP 3

Write the system in augmented matrix form

$$\begin{pmatrix} 2 & -1 & 1 & | & 7 \\ 4 & -2 & -1 & | & -1 \\ 1 & 3 & 2 & | & 25 \end{pmatrix}$$

STEP 4

Swap row 1 with row 2:

$$\begin{pmatrix} 4 & -2 & -1 & | & -1 \\ 2 & -1 & 1 & | & 7 \\ 1 & 3 & 2 & | & 25 \end{pmatrix}$$

STEP 5

Subtract $\frac{1}{2} \times$(row 1) from row 2:

$$\begin{pmatrix} 4 & -2 & -1 & | & -1 \\ 0 & 0 & \frac{3}{2} & | & \frac{15}{2} \\ 1 & 3 & 2 & | & 25 \end{pmatrix}$$

STEP 6

Multiply row 2 by $\frac{2}{3}$:

$$\begin{pmatrix} 4 & -2 & -1 & | & -1 \\ 0 & 0 & 1 & | & 5 \\ 1 & 3 & 2 & | & 25 \end{pmatrix}$$

STEP 7

Subtract $\frac{1}{4} \times$(row 1) from row 3:

$$\begin{pmatrix} 4 & -2 & -1 & | & -1 \\ 0 & 0 & 1 & | & 5 \\ 0 & \frac{7}{2} & \frac{9}{4} & | & \frac{101}{4} \end{pmatrix}$$

STEP 8

Multiply row 3 by 4:

$$\begin{pmatrix} 4 & -2 & -1 & | & -1 \\ 0 & 0 & 1 & | & 5 \\ 0 & 14 & 9 & | & 101 \end{pmatrix}$$

STEP 9

Swap row 2 with row 3:

$$\begin{pmatrix} 4 & -2 & -1 & | & -1 \\ 0 & 14 & 9 & | & 101 \\ 0 & 0 & 1 & | & 5 \end{pmatrix}$$

STEP 10

Subtract $9 \times$(row 3) from row 2:

$$\begin{pmatrix} 4 & -2 & -1 & | & -1 \\ 0 & 14 & 0 & | & 56 \\ 0 & 0 & 1 & | & 5 \end{pmatrix}$$

STEP 11

Divide row 2 by 14:

$$\begin{pmatrix} 4 & -2 & -1 & | & -1 \\ 0 & 1 & 0 & | & 4 \\ 0 & 0 & 1 & | & 5 \end{pmatrix}$$

STEP 12

Add $2 \times$(row 2) to row 1:

$$\begin{pmatrix} 4 & 0 & -1 & | & 7 \\ 0 & 1 & 0 & | & 4 \\ 0 & 0 & 1 & | & 5 \end{pmatrix}$$

STEP 13

Add row 3 to row 1:

$$\begin{pmatrix} 4 & 0 & 0 & | & 12 \\ 0 & 1 & 0 & | & 4 \\ 0 & 0 & 1 & | & 5 \end{pmatrix}$$

STEP 14

Divide row 1 by 4:

$$\begin{pmatrix} 1 & 0 & 0 & | & 3 \\ 0 & 1 & 0 & | & 4 \\ 0 & 0 & 1 & | & 5 \end{pmatrix}$$

STEP 15

Collect results:

Answer:

$$\begin{cases} x = 3 \\ y = 4 \\ z = 5 \end{cases}$$

5.3. Systems of Linear Equations and Determinants (Cramer's Rule)

Cramer's method is very useful for lineal systems of 2 variables as well as 3, 4, etc. Cramer's Rule is easy to demonstrate; the 2x2 case is the simplest one and can be extended to other cases. We will apply traditional elimination method to develop the Cramer's Rule. Let us consider the following system (2 x 2, which can be extended to 3 x 3, or more elements):

$$a_1 x + b_1 y = c_1$$
$$a_2 x + b_2 y = c_2$$

$$a_1 b_2 x + b_1 b_2 y = c_1 b_2$$
$$-a_2 b_1 x - b_2 b_1 y = -c_2 b_1$$

Multiply the first equation by b_2 and the second equation by $-b_1$ to eliminate $y - variable$

After multiplying, add both equations and solve for x:

$$b_2 x - a_2 b_1 x = c_1 b_2 - c_2 b_1$$
$$x(a_1 b_2 - a_2 b_1) = c_1 b_2 - c_2 b_1$$

$$x = \frac{c_1 b_2 - c_2 b_1}{a_1 b_2 - a_2 b_1}$$

$$x = \frac{\begin{vmatrix} c_1 & b_1 \\ c_2 & b_2 \end{vmatrix}}{\begin{vmatrix} a_1 & b_1 \\ a_2 & b_2 \end{vmatrix}}$$

$$x = \frac{D_x}{D} \quad y = \frac{D_y}{D}$$

The resulting solution is a fraction equivalent to a matrix (Determinant) operation, where D_x is called the Determinant for $x\ variable$: Check as follow, next page.

$$D_x = \begin{vmatrix} c_1 & b_1 \\ c_2 & b_2 \end{vmatrix} = (c_1 b_2 - c_2 b_1)$$

Equivalently for $y\ variable$

$$D_y = \begin{vmatrix} a_1 & c_1 \\ a_2 & c_2 \end{vmatrix} = (a_1 c_2 - a_2 c_1)$$

and for the system:

$$D_y = \begin{vmatrix} a_1 & b_1 \\ a_2 & b_2 \end{vmatrix} = (a_1 b_2 - a_2 b_1)$$

EXAMPLE USING WOLFRAM ALPHA ENGINE
APPLY CRAMER'S RULE.

Lets analyze previous example, but now using Cramer's Rule.

Input:

$\{2x - y + z = 7, 4x - 2y - z = -1, x + 3y + 2z = 25\}$

⬚ WolframlAlpha Step-by-Step Solution

Solutions:

STEP 1

Solve the following system:
$$\begin{cases} 2x - y + z = 7 \\ 4x - 2y - z = -1 \\ x + 3y + 2z = 25 \end{cases}$$

STEP 2

Express the system in matrix form:
$$\begin{pmatrix} 2 & -1 & 1 \\ 4 & -2 & -1 \\ 1 & 3 & 2 \end{pmatrix}\begin{pmatrix} x \\ y \\ z \end{pmatrix} = \begin{pmatrix} 7 \\ -1 \\ 25 \end{pmatrix}$$

STEP 3

Solve the system with Cramer's rule:
$$x = \frac{\begin{vmatrix} 7 & -1 & 1 \\ -1 & -2 & -1 \\ 25 & 3 & 2 \end{vmatrix}}{\begin{vmatrix} 2 & -1 & 1 \\ 4 & -2 & -1 \\ 1 & 3 & 2 \end{vmatrix}} \text{ and } y = \frac{\begin{vmatrix} 2 & 7 & 1 \\ 4 & -1 & -1 \\ 1 & 25 & 2 \end{vmatrix}}{\begin{vmatrix} 2 & -1 & 1 \\ 4 & -2 & -1 \\ 1 & 3 & 2 \end{vmatrix}} \text{ and } z = \frac{\begin{vmatrix} 2 & -1 & 7 \\ 4 & -2 & -1 \\ 1 & 3 & 25 \end{vmatrix}}{\begin{vmatrix} 2 & -1 & 1 \\ 4 & -2 & -1 \\ 1 & 3 & 2 \end{vmatrix}}$$

STEP 4

Evaluate the determinant $\begin{vmatrix} 2 & -1 & 1 \\ 4 & -2 & -1 \\ 1 & 3 & 2 \end{vmatrix} = 21$:

$$x = \frac{\begin{vmatrix} 7 & -1 & 1 \\ -1 & -2 & -1 \\ 25 & 3 & 2 \end{vmatrix}}{21} \text{ and } y = \frac{\begin{vmatrix} 2 & 7 & 1 \\ 4 & -1 & -1 \\ 1 & 25 & 2 \end{vmatrix}}{21} \text{ and } z = \frac{\begin{vmatrix} 2 & -1 & 7 \\ 4 & -2 & -1 \\ 1 & 3 & 25 \end{vmatrix}}{21}$$

STEP 5

Evaluate the determinant $\begin{vmatrix} 7 & -1 & 1 \\ -1 & -2 & -1 \\ 25 & 3 & 2 \end{vmatrix} = 63$:

$$x = \frac{63}{21} \text{ and } y = \frac{\begin{vmatrix} 2 & 7 & 1 \\ 4 & -1 & -1 \\ 1 & 25 & 2 \end{vmatrix}}{21} \text{ and } z = \frac{\begin{vmatrix} 2 & -1 & 7 \\ 4 & -2 & -1 \\ 1 & 3 & 25 \end{vmatrix}}{21}$$

STEP 6

Divide 63 by 21: $\dfrac{63}{21} = \dfrac{3 \times 21}{1 \times 21} = 3$:

$x = \boxed{3}$ and $y = \dfrac{\begin{vmatrix} 2 & 7 & 1 \\ 4 & -1 & -1 \\ 1 & 25 & 2 \end{vmatrix}}{21}$ and $z = \dfrac{\begin{vmatrix} 2 & -1 & 7 \\ 4 & -2 & -1 \\ 1 & 3 & 25 \end{vmatrix}}{21}$

STEP 7

Evaluate the determinant $\begin{vmatrix} 2 & 7 & 1 \\ 4 & -1 & -1 \\ 1 & 25 & 2 \end{vmatrix} = 84$:

$x = 3$ and $y = \dfrac{84}{21}$ and $z = \dfrac{\begin{vmatrix} 2 & -1 & 7 \\ 4 & -2 & -1 \\ 1 & 3 & 25 \end{vmatrix}}{21}$

STEP 8

Divide 84 by 21: $\dfrac{84}{21} = \dfrac{4 \times 21}{1 \times 21} = 4$:

$x = 3$ and $y = \boxed{4}$ and $z = \dfrac{\begin{vmatrix} 2 & -1 & 7 \\ 4 & -2 & -1 \\ 1 & 3 & 25 \end{vmatrix}}{21}$

STEP 9

Evaluate the determinant $\begin{vmatrix} 2 & -1 & 7 \\ 4 & -2 & -1 \\ 1 & 3 & 25 \end{vmatrix} = 105$:

$x = 3$ and $y = 4$ and $z = \dfrac{105}{21}$

STEP 10

Divide 105 by 21: $\dfrac{105}{21} = \dfrac{5 \times 21}{1 \times 21} = 5$:

Answer:

$x = 3$ and $y = 4$ and $z = 5$

5.4. System of Non-linear Equations

System of nonlinear equations can be solved by addition/subtraction and/or substitution. At least one equation will be second degree or higher equation.

EXAMPLE USING MICROSOFT MATHEMATICS ADD-IN
SOLVE THE FOLLOWING SYSTEM IN YOUR WORD DOC.

Solve by substituting y *value*

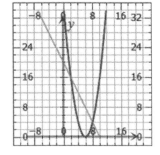

$$y = x^2 - 12x + 36$$
$$y = -2x + 20$$

So, we can write:

$$x^2 - 12x + 36 = -2x + 20$$
$$x^2 - 10x + 16 = 0$$

The solution of the resulting quadratic equation is:

$$x = 2 \; or \; x = 8$$

By substituting these values into the original equations, we get:

$$y = -2(2) + 20 = 16$$
$$y = -2(8) + 20 = 4$$

So the two interceptions (solutions) are:

$$(x = 2, y = 16) \; or \; (x = 8, y = 4)$$

Similar to the previous example, systems of nonlinear equations can be solved using any of the describes applications an/or software above in the context of this guide.

Despite the simplicity of what is exposed in this guide, I hope to help you learn mathematics, especially those who do not like it, using the tools available on the internet, applying technology to facilitate learning in addition to speeding up the solution of mathematical problems.

Thank you very much for your opinion.

Professor Prieto-Valdes

Made in United States
Orlando, FL
12 September 2024

51454152R00063